Paleoecology of an
Early Pleistocene Lake

The printing of this volume
has been made possible through
generous contributions to the Memoir Fund of
The Geological Society of America,
and is partially supported by a grant from
The National Science Foundation

The Geological Society of America, Inc.
Memoir 113

Paleoecology of an Early Pleistocene Lake on the High Plains of Texas, *1969.*

Roger Y. Anderson,
University of New Mexico, Albuquerque, New Mexico

and

Douglas W. Kirkland
Mobil Research and Development Corporation, Dallas, Texas

Editors

1969

© Copyright 1969, The Geological Society of America, Inc.
(Copyright is not claimed on any material prepared by
U.S. Government employees within the scope of their employment.)
Library of Congress Catalog Card Number 79-98523
S.B.N. 8137-1113-4

Published by
THE GEOLOGICAL SOCIETY OF AMERICA
Colorado Building, P.O. Box 1719
Boulder, Colorado 80302

Printed in the United States of America

Acknowledgments

Assistance was obtained from a number of individuals who have not contributed a formal paper to the final report. J. T. Hughes, Curator of Paleontology at the Panhandle-Plains Historical Museum allowed us to review his field notes, loaned his Rita Blanca fossil collection, and discussed various aspects of the study. J. L. Kunkler, Quality of Water Branch of the U.S. Geological Survey, helped with quantitative analysis problems, C. F. Dodge with X-ray analysis, and R. L. Stone with differential thermal analysis. The following individuals contributed fossil identifications at some stage in the project: D. J. Borrer, Ohio State University (Odonata); R. H. Clisby, Oberlin College (pollen); R. J. Drake, University of British Columbia (Mollusca); H. E. Evans, Museum of Comparative Ecology, Harvard College (Hymenoptera); C. C. Hoff, University of New Mexico (Ostracoda); R. E. Peck, University of Missouri (Ostracoda); W. D. Pierce, Los Angeles County Museum (Insecta); D. W. Price, University of California, Berkeley (Insecta); Alan Stone, Entomology Research Branch, U.S. Department of Agriculture, Washington, D.C. (Culicidae); D. W. Taylor, U.S. National Museum (Mollusca); J. M. White, Del Mar College (Culicidae); R. H. Whitsel, San Mateo County Mosquito Abatement District, Burlingame, California (Insecta); M. J. Westfall, University of Florida (Odonata); W. W. Wirth, Entomology Research Branch, U.S. Department of Agriculture, Washington, D.C. (Culicidae); C. D. Wise, Ball State Teachers College (Ostracoda). E. S. Deevey, Jr., Yale University suggested several sources for fossil identification, and W. N. Blair, U.S. Geological Survey, Menlo Park, California, collected many of the fossil specimens.

The work of the editors was supported by research grants from the National Science Foundation. They are grateful for the freedom and latitude allowed under the grants.

Foreword

Geology, being an historical science, gains in depth only when its practitioners investigate their particular section of the record in exceptional depth. What we learn from one epoch is applicable to all parts of the column. But what we learn from the youngest part of the geologic record is peculiarly valuable because it can be illuminated with considerable assurance by our understanding of the physical and biological processes that operate today.

Anderson and Kirkland have put us much in their debt for their penetrating, and all but exhaustive, reconstruction of an early Pleistocene lake on the High Plains of Texas. Some measure of the concentration of this study may be gained from the fact that, in addition to themselves, they enlisted the collaboration of 10 specialists, all of whom focused their study, primarily, on a column of sediment about 4.5 feet thick and only a few hundred yards in lateral extent. To be sure, this is an altogether remarkable section of lake beds — remarkable for its annual, indeed, seasonal record of events throughout some 1,400 years and remarkable also for the richness of its flora and fauna. The specialists include not only botanists, entomologists, a palynologist, and an ichthyologist, but also a geochemist and a mathematician.

By integrating the conclusions and judgments of all the participants in the study, Anderson and Kirkland have derived a satisfying picture of the environment of this small and relatively short-lived lake. Among other interesting and useful things, they have proved by five independent lines of evidence that the pairs of thin laminae in these lake beds represent annual increments of sediment, that is, that they are in fact varves. This point is hammered down, and the nails are clinched on the other side. From this substantial platform they go on to shed light on the limnology of the lake and the geographic shifts in the dominant elements of the fossil flora. Also, they indicate the sorts of ecological factors that may have exerted the control. Their cautiously tentative interpretation of the probable climate, and its cyclic fluctuations, strike me as an especially valuable contribution to knowledge.

Anderson and Kirkland are to be commended for an exceptionally competent piece of work and for the critical attitude they show toward their own judgments and conclusions — a criticality in the best tradition of science.

W. H. BRADLEY
October 1966

Preface

This study began in 1960 when a sample of laminated lake clay was brought to the editors' attention by Jerry Harbour, a contributor to this report. After collecting additional material and spending several weeks work on the micro-stratigraphic position of the fossils associated with the laminae, we tentatively concluded that the layers were annual. The relation of these annual layers, to organisms and environment, is the theme of this report.

The relationships between organisms and environment can best be studied in the living state. One important reason for attempting paleoecological studies, however, is that a fourth dimension can be added to our understanding of ecologic processes. The presence of annual laminations in the Rita Blanca deposits provides a framework for the study of the temporal relationships of some of these processes.

The original purpose of this investigation was to determine the nature of climatic change as reflected by variations in varve thickness. Further study, however, showed that lithologic factors could not be separated from biologic factors and also revealed the truth of Hecker's admonition that "paleoecological and lithological investigation must be conducted side by side."

The expanded scope of the investigation required the participation of a number of specialists and each article in this report reflects the contribution of a specialist. This format was chosen in order to document interpretations and conclusions and to give proper credits to sources of information.

Although an attempt was made to conduct a comprehensive study, there are still many aspects that were not investigated or that could be improved, and only limitation of time and resources brought the project to a close. This is especially true of the investigation of organic matter. Infra-red absorption, for example, and chromatographic techniques would have given a much better idea of the type and distribution of organic matter. Also, the absolute rate and variation of pollen and algae accumulation remains to be determined in detail. Several other techniques are also applicable. Nevertheless, the editors feel that the present report is a moderately complete reconstruction of the ancient lake.

R. Y. ANDERSON
D. W. KIRKLAND

ix

Contents

Page

ABSTRACT 1
PART I. INTRODUCTION.. 3
Geologic setting of the Rita Blanca lake deposits.
By Roger Y. Anderson and Douglas W. Kirkland........................ 3
PART II. PETROLOGY... 15
Composition and origin of the Rita Blanca varves.
By Douglas W. Kirkland and Roger Y. Anderson....................... 15
Carbon and oxygen isotopic composition of carbonate material in the
Rita Blanca varves. By Jon N. Weber................................. 47
Statistical analysis of the Rita Blanca varve time-series.
By Roger Y. Anderson and L. H. Koopmans........................... 59
PART III. PALEONTOLOGY... 77
Systematic list of fossils in the Rita Blanca lake deposits.
By Douglas W. Kirkland and Roger Y. Anderson....................... 77
Pollen profile of the Rita Blanca lake deposits. By Jerry Harbour.............. 83
Oak leaves of the Rita Blanca lake deposits. By John M. Tucker............... 97
Fossil flora of the Rita Blanca lake deposits. By William C. Martin...........101
Ostracodes of the Rita Blanca lake deposits. By Richard H. Benson...........107
Aquatic insects of the Rita Blanca lake deposits. By James E. Sublette..........117
Terrestrial insects of the Rita Blanca lake deposits. By Floyd G. Werner........123
Two new Cleoninae from the Rita Blanca lake deposits (Coleoptera:
Curculionidae). By Elbert L. Sleeper..................................131
Fishes of the Rita Blanca lake deposits. By William J. Koster.................135
PART IV. SYNTHESIS..141
Paleoecology of the Rita Blanca lake area.
By Roger Y. Anderson and Douglas W. Kirkland........................141
APPENDIX I. Summary of analyses of parameters determined in the Rita
Blanca varve series on a 5-year or 20-year sampling interval...............200
APPENDIX II. Thickness in millimeters of the Rita Blanca varve series............204
SUBJECT INDEX 209
SYSTEMATIC INDEX 213

ILLUSTRATIONS

FIGURES

1. Index map of Rita Blanca lake deposits................................. 4
2. Diagrams illustrating the formation of deflation basins and lacustrine deposits.. 9
3. Isopachous map of part of the varved sequence.......................... 11

4. Map showing relation of exposed varved sediments to inferred limits of
   Rita Blanca Lake.. 12
5. Stratigraphic columns of lower exposed lake beds and calcareous claystone
   unit, and diagrammatic illustration of varve........................... 16
6. Frequency distribution of varve thickness.............................. 18
7. Approximate composition of the light- and dark-colored layers of a varve
   from a carbonate-rich clay section.................................... 19
8. Approximate composition of the light- and dark-colored layers of a varve
   from a carbonate-poor clay section.................................... 20
9. Compositional variation of light- and dark-colored laminae in
   different parts of varve series.. 21
10. Superimposed histograms of varve thickness from Localities A and B........ 22
11. Differential thermograms of a Rita Blanca varve sample run in a
    nitrogen atmosphere and in air....................................... 25
12. Histogram showing calcium and magnesium variation in a sequence of
    four varves 27
13. Frequency curve showing variation in length of silt grains............... 29
14. Diagram of Rita Blanca varves perpendicular to bedding.................. 31
15. Curves showing variation of varve thickness with time................... 39
16. Smoothed curves showing variation of percent calcium carbonate and
    of color index with time.. 40
17. Variation of "absolute" rate of clay deposition and of calcium
    carbonate deposition with time....................................... 42
18. Variation in "absolute" rate of tannin-lignin and of organic nitrogen
    accumulation with time.. 43
19. Variation of carbon and oxygen isotopic composition with time,
    40-year intervals 53
20. Variation of carbon and oxygen isotopic composition with time,
    60-year intervals 54
21. Variation of carbon and oxygen isotopic composition with time,
    80-year periods 55
22. Variation of carbon and oxygen isotopic composition with time,
    100-year periods 56
23. Fourier spectrum of laminae thickness................................. 63
24. Fourier spectrum of clay thickness.................................... 64
25. Fourier spectrum of calcium carbonate thickness........................ 65
26. Fourier spectrum of the 200-unit thickness series....................... 67
27. Power spectra of the eight parameters determined in the Rita Blanca
    varve series 69
28. Coefficients of coherence of all combinations of the eight parameters
    determined in the Rita Blanca varve series............................ 70
29. Average coherence values for each of the eight parameters and for all 28
    cross-spectrum estimates in the Rita Blanca varve series................ 73
30. Phase angles for clay–calcium carbonate coherence coefficients........... 74
31. Pollen profile of the Rita Blanca lake deposits......................... 84
32. Relationship of altitudinal floral associations to climatic conditions along a
    zone of equal latitude.. 89
33. Relationship between sediment composition and the partial pollen profile
    in the varved part of the Rita Blanca lake beds........................ 91
34. Variation of various biotic and mineral fractions in the Rita Blanca
    varve series 149

PLATES

1. Photomicrographs of Rita Blanca varve sections..........................161
2. Correlation of varves between Localities A and B........................162
3. Photomicrograph of upper bedding plane of a light-colored laminae...........163
4. Outcrop of varved Rita Blanca lake deposits..............................164
5. Differential thermograms of the Rita Blanca varved section........Facing page 164
6. Variation with time of carbon and oxygen isotopic composition of the carbonate portion of the Rita Blanca varves.................Facing page 164
7. Graph of variations in eight parameters determined in Rita Blanca varve series.................................Facing page 164
8. Rita Blanca pollen and spores...167
9. Rita Blanca pollen, alga, and oak leaves...............................168
10. Rita Blanca leaves, inflorescences, and stems...........................171
11. Rita Blanca leaves and achene 172
12. Rita Blanca Odonata 175
13. Rita Blanca Trichoptera and Diptera...................................176
14. Rita Blanca Diptera (Chironomidae)....................................179
15. Rita Blanca Diptera (Chironomidae)....................................180
16. Rita Blanca Diptera, Hemiptera, Homoptera, and Coleoptera.................183
17. Rita Blanca Coleoptera, Diptera, and Homoptera..........................184
18. Rita Blanca Diptera and Hymenoptera 187
19. Rita Blanca Hymenoptera 188
20. Rita Blanca Hymenoptera and Coleoptera................................191
21. Rita Blanca ostracodes 192
22. Rita Blanca ostracodes 195
23. Rita Blanca fish 196
24. Rita Blanca ostracodes and pelecypods..................................199

TABLES

1. Cenozoic stratigraphy of the southern High Plains......................... 7
2. Tannin-lignin content of light- and dark-colored laminae from light and dark zones of the Rita Blanca deposits................................ 26
3. Pollen and spore variation in light- and dark-colored laminae from Rita Blanca varve series... 34
4. Characteristics of varves in Recent nonglacial lakes....................... 35
5. Carbon and oxygen isotopic composition of light- and dark-colored laminae in Rita Blanca varves.. 49
6. Linear regression and correlation analysis of isotope ratios with other parameters measured in Rita Blanca varve series....................... 49
7. Correlation coefficients for all possible correlations among eight parameters determined in the Rita Blanca varve series............................ 68
8. Comparison of the aquatic insect fauna of Rita Blanca Lake with insects from meromictic lakes 121

Abstract

The early Pleistocene (Blancan) Rita Blanca lake deposits in the north-western part of the Panhandle of Texas occupy a deflation basin cut through the caprock of the Pliocene Ogallala Group. During its maximum development, Rita Blanca lake had an elliptical shape with a north-south length of about 6 miles and a breadth of about 3.5 miles.

The lower exposures of the Rita Blanca deposits contain an areally restricted clay bed with a maximum observed thickness of 65 inches that contains abundant fossils representing the lacustrine and riparian environments, and a plains community of mixed sagebrush and grass. The clay bed also contains two types of cyclic lithology: (1) an alternation of light- and dark-colored clay zones on the scale of centimeters and decimeters, and (2) couplets of light- and dark-colored laminae with an average thickness of 0.9 mm.

The light-colored laminae are rich in calcium carbonate, quartz silt grains, and ostracodes; the dark-colored laminae are composed principally of illite and organic matter. The laminae can be correlated with little change over 300 yards, and changes in the proportion of the constituents are responsible for the larger scale cyclic bedding.

The microstratigraphic position and associations of the ostracodes *Limnocythere, Cyprideis,* and *Candona,* deciduous leaves of oak (*Quercus*) and willow (*Salix*), *Artemisia* pollen, pupae and adults of Chironomidae (midges), and carbon and oxygen isotope ratios demonstrate that the light-colored high-carbonate laminae were deposited in the summer and the dark-colored low-carbonate laminae were deposited in the winter and spring.

A saline temporary hard-water lake is suggested by sediment composition and by four kinds of fossils that customarily reflect a saline or alkaline environment but are not necessarily restricted to it (*Ruppia maritima*, ditch grass; *Fundulus,* killifish; *Limnocythere* and *Cyprideis,* ostracodes; a species of *Chironomus,* midge). The entire fossil assemblage, with the exception of fungal spores, was transported to site of deposition in the profundal zone of the lake. The absence of a benthonic fauna, the distinct laminations and the saline character of the water suggests meromixis.

The continuous 1,400-year varve series was sampled on a time-series basis and the long-term associations subjected to regression, Fourier, and bi-spectral

1

analysis. Clay is negatively associated with calcium carbonate for intervals longer than 60-70 years, whereas the association is positive for short-term changes — which is interpreted to mean that some calcium carbonate was washed in with the clay but the long-term changes in carbonate were the result of carbonate precipitation in the lake. Harmonic analysis of couplet thickness revealed a moderately well-defined 22-year period that was also present in the carbonate fraction but not in the clay fraction.

Seasonal and long-term associations of clay, silt, carbonate, organic matter, fungal spores, and ostracodes parallel each other, and the negative long-term association of clay and carbonate is interpreted as intervals of cool-moist climate alternating with intervals of warm-dry climate. The fossils and lithologic changes suggest a climatic regime with cooler temperatures and with the same or less moisture than the present area receives today, but with most of the moisture arriving in the cool season rather than in the warm season.

Part I. Introduction

Geologic Setting of the Rita Blanca Lake Deposits

ROGER Y. ANDERSON

University of New Mexico, Albuquerque, New Mexico

DOUGLAS W. KIRKLAND

Mobil Research and Development Corporation, Dallas, Texas

INTRODUCTION

The Rita Blanca lake deposits occur in the northwestern part of the Texas Panhandle in Hartley County about 6 miles west of Channing, Texas (Fig. 1). The stratigraphic section that is described in this report is exposed in several places along Mathews and Mustang draws (Fig. 3). The best exposure occurs in Mustang draw about 30 yards east of the junction of the two streams along a north-facing cliff (Fig. 3, Loc. A).

The petrology of the Rita Blanca deposit has been described in a general way by Evans and Meade (1945, p. 493) and Johnston and Savage (1955, p. 40). Plant and invertebrate fossils from a laminated clay in the lower part of the section have not previously been identified, although their presence has been noted by Evans and Meade (1945, p. 493 and 503), Johnston and Savage (1955), and Carpenter (1957, p. 116). Vertebrate fossils of Blancan age occurring in weakly consolidated sandstone overlying the laminated clay have been listed by Evans and Meade and by Johnston and Savage. Childs Frick has made extensive vertebrate collections from several quarries in the district, and small collections have been made by the West Texas Museum, Lubbock, Texas, and the Panhandle-Plains Historical Museum, Canyon, Texas. In December 1958, Jerry Harbour collected 3-inch channel samples

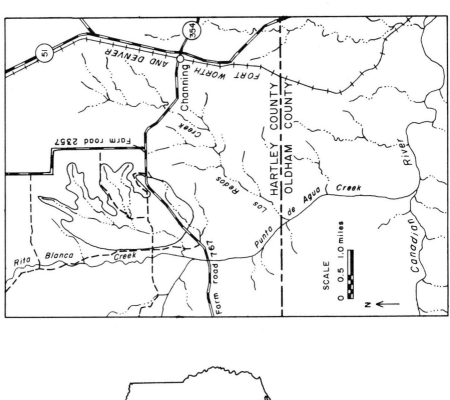

Figure 1. Index map of Rita Blanca lake deposits.

throughout the laminated section. Pollen separation was done by Harbour at the Geochronology Laboratory of the University of Arizona. His results are contained in an article in this report.

According to Carpenter (1957, p. 116) the first insect specimens from the laminated shale were found by Roy Reinhart of Miami University (Ohio).

The most important general work relating to the Rita Blanca lake beds of Hartley County is *Quaternary of the Texas High Plains* by G. L. Evans and G. E. Meade (1945). In 1940 and 1941 they determined that the Blanco beds of Crosby County, Texas, were laid down in a lake basin. Recognition of a lacustrine origin for these beds led to a search for, and discovery of, other ancient filled lakes, including the Rita Blanca deposit.

REGIONAL STRATIGRAPHY AND GEOLOGIC HISTORY

A complex of fluvial sediment from the Rocky Mountains was deposited on the High Plains during late Miocene? and Pliocene time. These deposits, termed the Ogallala Group, generally consist of fine- to medium-grained sand and local gravel (Frye and Leonard, 1957a, p. 3) deposited on an erosion surface developed on Mesozoic and Permian rocks. In the Panhandle of Texas, the thickness of the Ogallala Group ranges from 50 to 350 feet (Evans, 1956, p. 16).

The uppermost unit of the Ogallala is a flood-plain–channel complex that buried all elements of the former topography and has a caliche soil horizon at the top containing up to 60 percent calcium carbonate (Frye and Leonard, 1965).

Stream deposition in the Panhandle area essentially ceased about the end of middle Pliocene time because of an increasingly arid climate and stream piracy (Evans, 1956, p. 16). During the upper Pliocene, a thick and wide-spread mantle of dense calcium carbonate, generally termed "caprock," was developed by soil-forming processes on a featureless plain (Brown, 1956, p. 2). During this period of stability, the surface of the southern High Plains was modified by the formation of deflation basins.

The dry environment of the late Pliocene was interrupted by what is judged to be the sharpest climatic change of the late Cenozoic (Frye and Leonard, 1957a, p. 6). The initiation of pluvial conditions marks the break between the Pliocene and Pleistocene in the southern High Plains, and the process of basin formation by deflation during dry periods and the formation of lakes and lacustrine sediments during humid periods continued throughout the Pleistocene.

Continental glaciers moved as far south as northeastern Kansas in the Nebraskan, while in the southern High Plains deflation basins became lakes. Frye and Leonard (1965, p. 208) in their survey of the Nebraskan of the High Plains make no mention of lake deposits and have on another occasion

(1957b) suggested that the Rita Blanca deposits are of fluvial origin. However, a variety of life forms and the petrology indicate a lacustrine origin for the lower part of the section.

During the Kansan age, the lacustrine Tule Formation formed in deflation basins in the Panhandle area. In Briscoe and Swisher Counties, Texas, the Tule Formation accumulated in a lake which, at maximum development, occupied an area of more than 40 square miles (Evans, 1956, p. 26). In Hartley County, beds equivalent in age to the Tule Formation overlie the Rita Blanca deposits. The Pearlette volcanic ash fell during late Kansan or earliest Yarmouthian time and was deposited on the Ogallala Group or on the Tule Formation and its equivalents in the southern High Plains.

The Tahoka Clay, a lake deposit of Wisconsin age, consists of calcareous, bentonitic clay and sand, and was deposited in all of the large basins and in many of the shallow playas existing on the present Plains surface (Table 1). Wendorf (1961, p. 130) estimates that the Tahoka Clay was deposited 15,000 to 22,500 years before the present.

Deflation has been active in the southern High Plains during the Recent. At irregular intervals, the wind-formed basins become playa lakes, but within a relatively short period of time the water evaporates, leaving mud flats exposed to wind activity.

AGE OF THE RITA BLANCA LAKE DEPOSITS

Quaternary lacustrine deposits in the southern High Plains range from earliest Pleistocene to Recent in age. The deposits in these depressions contain the most complete sequence of Pleistocene continental faunas yet recorded (Taylor, 1960, p. 18). The oldest Pleistocene lacustrine deposits recognized in the Texas Panhandle are dated as Blancan in age by their vertebrate fauna. The term "Blancan" was proposed as a provincial time term (Wood and others, 1941, p. 12) for mammalian assemblages considered roughly contemporaneous and characterized by the association of *Stegomastodon* and *Nannippus* among others. General agreement exists among paleontologists concerning the similarity of faunas classed as Blancan in Texas, Kansas, and Nebraska (Frye and Leonard, 1952, p. 66).

The laminated clays of the Rita Blanca deposit are directly overlain by gray calcareous sandstone and mudstone which contain mammal bones of several short-ranging genera found in the Blanco Formation of Crosby County (Evans, 1949, p. 9), the type locality for the Blancan provincial age. The known Blancan mammals from the Rita Blanca deposit are *Stegomastodon, Equus (Plesippus)* cf. *E. simplicidens, Nannippus* cf. *N. phlegon,* and *Gigantocamelus* cf. *G. spatulus* (Johnston and Savage, 1955, p. 40). Although the Rita Blanca mammalian genera range into the Kansan, both Evans and Meade (1945, p. 493) and Frye and Leonard (1965, p. 208) consider the deposits

TABLE 1. CENOZOIC STRATIGRAPHY OF THE SOUTHERN HIGH PLAINS
(MODIFIED FROM FRYE AND LEONARD, 1957b, AND EVANS, 1949).

Series	Pleistocene ages	North American ages	Rock unit	Sedimentary environment
Pleistocene	Recent interglacial	Rancholabrean	Dune sand	Aeolian
Pleistocene	Wisconsin glacial	Rancholabrean	Tahoka Clay	Lacustrine
Pleistocene	Sangamon interglacial	Rancholabrean		
Pleistocene	Illinoian glacial	Irvingtonian		
Pleistocene	Yarmouth interglacial	Irvingtonian		
Pleistocene	Kansan glacial	Irvingtonian	Pearlette volcanic ash / Tule Formation	Lacustrine
Pleistocene	Aftonian interglacial	Blancan		
Pleistocene	Nebraskan glacial	Blancan	Rita Blanca deposit / Blanco Formation	Lacustrine
Pliocene	Upper	Blancan		
Pliocene	Middle	Hemphillian	Ogallala Group	Fluvial
Pliocene	Lower	Hemphillian		

to be correlative with the Blanco beds in Crosby County, Texas, hence Blancan in age. Deevey (1965, p. 649) states that the deposits are dated only roughly as early Pleistocene, but the typical Blancan mammals and opinions of the previous workers suggest that the Blancan assignment is reasonably certain.

The Blancan faunas have been assigned by some workers (Schultz and Stout, 1941, 1945, 1948; McGrew, 1944; Evans and Meade, 1945; Evans, 1948; Frye and others, 1948; Frye and Leonard, 1952, 1957a) to early Pleistocene time and by others to late Pliocene time (Hibbard, 1937, 1941;

Frye and Hibbard, 1941). In regard to the age of the Blanco beds of Crosby County, Texas, Evans (1948, p. 619) states: "The Blanco beds evidently represent a period of relative humidity preceded and succeeded by periods of relative aridity. This condition suggests a glacial stage, and the faunal evidence precludes any but the first glacial as the time of Blanco Deposition." According to Frye and Leonard (1952, p. 67):

Three independent kinds of evidence, exclusive of fossil vertebrates, demonstrate that the Blanco formation in central and southwestern Kansas and in northwestern Texas, is a product of the Nebraskan cycle of deposition and should be classed within the Nebraskan Stage. These are: (1) the contained fossil mollusks, (2) stratigraphic framing between the conclusively correlated Sappa member of the Meade formation[1] above (based on Pearlette volcanic ash, fossil mollusks, buried soil, and physiographic position) and the Pliocene Ogallala formation below, and (3) regional physiographic history.

Hibbard (1955, p. 183), taking a conservative stand on Pleistocene age assignments, states:

Only tentative correlation exists at the present time in North America between the glacial and interglacial deposits of the glacial region and the nonglacial deposits of the Ice Age (Pleistocene) outside of the glaciated regions. . . . Until more work is done and a better correlation exists between these regions it is considered best to treat the assignment of the Pleistocene faunas from southwestern Kansas to definite glacial or interglacial ages as only tentative.

An absolute age of the Rita Blanca deposits between 1.5 and 3.5 m.y. has been determined indirectly by the association of Blancan mammals with volcanic rocks in California and western Nevada (Evernden and others, 1964).

ORIGIN OF THE RITA BLANCA LAKE BASIN

Thousands of comparatively shallow depressions dot the surface of the southern High Plains. Over most of this area, the surface run-off accumulates in ephemeral lakes. The drainage area of individual basins ranges from only a few acres for the smallest to more than 100 square miles for the largest (Evans and Meade, 1945, p. 486). Patton (1935, p. 451) noted that there were two main types of basins: (1) elliptical depressions 10 to 50 feet deep and 0.125 to 0.5 mile in diameter, and (2) linear-shaped depressions 100 feet or more in depth and 1 to 3 miles long. Johnson (1901) and Baker (1915, p. 47) believed that the depressions were caused by sinking of the surface due to solution of Permian evaporites. Evans and Meade (1945, p. 486–490) and Judson (1950) have shown that most of the basins owe their origin in large part to deflation and not to the solution of evaporites at depth.

---

[1]The Sappa Member of the Meade Formation of southwestern Kansas is equivalent in age to the Tule Formation of northwestern Texas.

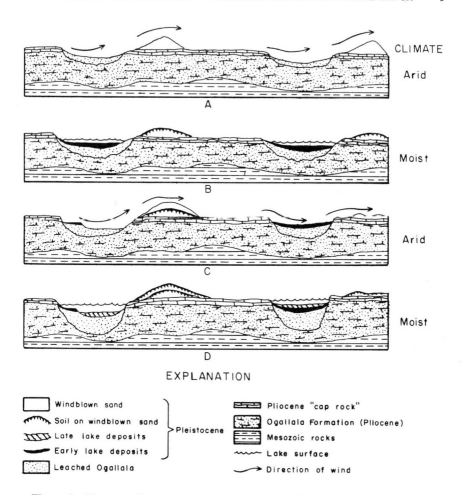

Figure 2. Diagrams illustrating the formation of deflation basins and lacustrine deposits (modified from Judson, 1950).

Figure 2 illustrates the effects of climate on development of the basins and lakes. Interestingly, the lake sediments exhibit unusual stratigraphic relations. The younger lake beds overlie the Ogallala stratigraphically but occupy a lower topographic position than the highest Ogallala sediments, and in the left-hand basin of Figure 2 the younger lake beds occupy a lower topographic position than the older lake beds.

Evans and Meade (1945, p. 490) state, "The basins containing the older deposits, so far as they can be recognized in exposure, are within the size and depth range of the larger, partly filled, more modern basins and are believed to owe their origin to the same cause." Judson (1950) made a detailed study of the present basins in Quay and Curry Counties, New Mexico, an area about 35 miles west of the Rita Blanca deposit. He states (p. 271):

It is entirely reasonable that depressions have been forming on the Plains since the end of the Pliocene. Some have ceased to grow and have become so choked with deposits that there may be little recognizable surface expression. Were the surficial cover stripped from the Plains, the resulting surface should be literally pock-marked with the open scars of modern depressions and the healed or partially healed scars of "extinct" depressions. The depression is not only characteristic of the Plains of the present, but also of the past back to the beginning of the Pleistocene.

Not all the events involved in the origin and filling of the Rita Blanca basin have been recorded in the stratigraphic record, and any account of the sequence of events that took place must be oversimplified. However, the following account is accurate insofar as is known: (1) the general climate of the upper Pliocene was dry, but occasional periods of increased rainfall leached the "caprock" and weakly cemented Ogallala sedimentary rocks; (2) strong winds and a weakened vegetative cover resulted in deflation of the leached area during drier periods. A maximum thickness of about 150 feet of Ogallala sediments was removed to form the Rita Blanca basin; (3) sometime in the early Pleistocene, conditions became more humid and a lake formed in the Rita Blanca basin. The basin was nearly filled with sediments during this phase; (4) a return to drier conditions resulted in the deflation of the weakly cemented lacustrine sediments and partial re-excavation of the basin; (5) humid conditions returned during the Kansan Age, and a permanent lake again formed in the Rita Blanca basin and filled with sediments; (6) the Pearlette ash fall in late Kansan or early Yarmouthian time filled the basin to a level approaching that of the surrounding plains (Frye and others, 1948, p. 519); (7) tributaries of the Canadian River breached the lake sediments in late Pleistocene time (Fig. 1) preventing the formation of lake sediments of Wisconsin age.

EXTENT AND GENERAL CHARACTERISTICS
OF THE RITA BLANCA DEPOSITS

The inferred extent of the Rita Blanca deposits is shown in Figure 4. At its maximum level, Rita Blanca Lake may have had a length of about 6 miles, a width of 3.5 miles, and an area of about 16 square miles. The eastern margin of the deposit is covered, but lacustrine sediments are absent in Los Redos Canyon to the east (Fig. 4). The inferred limits are partially based on the observation of Patton (1935, p. 451) that the larger Recent deflation basins on the southern High Plains are elongate.

Several criteria were used to distinguish the Pleistocene lacustrine beds from the Pliocene fluvial beds. The lithology and elements of the fossil flora and fauna of the laminated section are definitely lacustrine. The lake beds are generally light gray or white, whereas the Ogallala sandstone is reddish brown. The Ogallala in the vicinity of the Rita Blanca deposit generally consists of fine-grained sandstone, in some samples containing up to 5 percent lithic fragments; the lacustrine deposits are more varied and contain beds of dolomite, limestone, clay, and sandstone. Slump structures, probably caused by subaqueous sliding of lake sediments, are commonly exhibited by calcareous claystone and argillaceous limestone beds. A characteristic digitate drainage and erosion pattern in the lake sediments is caused by the absence of "caprock" and the less resistant nature of most of the lake sediments (Fig. 1).

The predominant lithology of the lake beds is fine-grained sand and sandstone. Calcareous claystone and argillaceous limestone are common in the lower exposed section. Precise stratigraphic relations are difficult to determine because facies and thickness changes occur within relatively short distances and because exposures are limited.

The contact between the Rita Blanca beds and the underlying Ogallala Group is not exposed. The laminated section of the Rita Blanca beds, which lies near the base of the exposed beds, is about 125 feet below the Pearlette ash, topographically and apparently stratigraphically. The maximum *possible* depth of water during deposition of the laminated unit was probably not much greater than 125 feet; the actual depth was probably less. Figure 5 is a measured section of beds immediately above and below the laminated section.

The laminated clay section occurs below sands and calcareous sandstone. This unit, which is 4.5 feet thick at Locality A (Fig. 3), thins toward the east at a rate of about 4 inches per 100 yards. At Locality A the laminated clay bed is nearly horizontal, but in other exposures it dips toward the west at about 1°–2°. The exposed laminated sections occur west of the center of the inferred Rita Blanca Lake (Fig. 4).

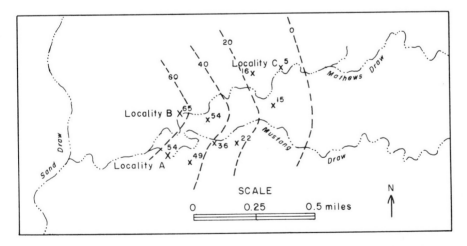

Figure 3. Isopachous map of part of the varved sequence, showing location of varve localities; contour interval 20 inches.

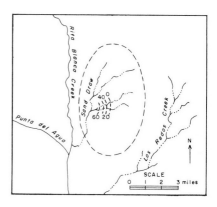

Figure 4. Map showing relation of exposed varved sediments (isopachous lines) to inferred limits of Rita Blanca Lake (dashed line); contour interval, 20 inches.

The section at Locality A (Fig. 3) was selected for detailed study because it is highly fossiliferous and well exposed. Few fossils were found at other exposures, except at Locality C, which contains abundant shells and fragments of *Physa*.

REFERENCES CITED

Baker, F. C., 1915, Pleistocene mollusks from Illinois: Nautilus, v. 29, p. 87–88

Brown, C. N., 1956, The origin of caliche on the northeastern Llano Estacado, Texas: Jour. Geology, v. 64, no. 1, p. 1–15

Carpenter, F. M., 1957, A Pliocene insect deposit in Texas: Psyche, v. 64, no. 3, p. 116

Deevey, E. S., Jr., 1965, Pleistocene nonmarine environments, *in* Wright, H. E., and Frey, D. G., *Editors,* The Quaternary of the United States: Princeton, Princeton Univ. Press, p. 643–652

Evans, G. L., 1948, Geology of the Blanco beds of West Texas, *in* Colbert, E. H., *Editor,* Pleistocene of the Great Plains (symposium): Geol. Soc. America Bull., v. 59, no. 6, p. 617–619

—— 1949, Upper Cenozoic of the High Plains (Texas), *in* Cenozoic geology of the Llano Estacado and Rio Grande Valley: West Tex. Geol. Soc. and N. Mex. Geol. Soc., field trip no. 2, p. 1–9

—— 1956, Cenozoic geology, *in* Eastern Llano Estacado and adjoining Osage Plains (Texas): West Tex. Geol. Soc. and Lubbock Geol. Soc., spring field trip, p. 16–26

Evans, G. L., and Meade, G. E., 1945, Quarternary of the Texas High Plains: Univ. Texas Pub. 4401, p. 485–507

Evernden, J. F., Savage, D. E., Curtis, G. H., and James, G. T., 1964, Potassium-argon dates and the Cenozoic mammalian chronology of North America: Am. Jour. Sci., v. 262, no. 2, p. 145–198

Frye, J. C., and Hibbard, C. W., 1941, Pliocene and Pleistocene stratigraphy and paleontology of the Meade basin, southwestern Kansas: Kans. Geol. Survey Bull. 38, pt. 13, p. 389–424

Frye, J. C., and Leonard, A. B., 1952, Pleistocene geology of Kansas: Kans. Geol. Survey Bull. 99, 230 p.

—— 1957a, Ecological interpretations of Pliocene and Pleistocene stratigraphy in the Great Plains region: Am. Jour. Sci., v. 255, p. 1–11

—— 1957b, Studies of Cenozoic geology along eastern margin of Texas High Plains, Armstrong to Howard Counties: Univ. Texas Bur. Econ. Geology, Rept. Inv. 32, 62 p.

—— 1965, Quaternary of the southern Great Plains, in Wright, H. E., and Frey, D. G., Editors, The Quaternary of the United States: Princeton, Princeton Univ. Press, p. 203–216

Frye, J. C., Swineford, Eda, and Leonard, A. E., 1948, Correlations, Pleistocene of Great Plains with glacial section: Jour. Geology, v. 56, no. 6, p. 501–525

Hibbard, C. W., 1937, An upper Pliocene fauna from Meade County, Kansas: Kans. Acad. Sci. Trans., v. 40, p. 239–265

—— 1941, Paleoecology and correlation of the Rexroad fauna from the upper Pliocene of southwestern Kansas as indicated by the mammals: Kans. Univ. Sci. Bull., v. 27, no. 6, p. 79–104

—— 1955, The Jinglebob interglacial (Sangamon?) fauna from Kansas and its climatic significance: Mich. Univ. Mus. Paleontology Contr., v. 12, no. 10, p. 170–228

Johnson, W. D., 1901, The High Plains and their utilization: U.S. Geol. Survey Ann. Rept. 21, pt. 4, p. 601–741

Johnston, C. S., and Savage, D. E., 1955, Introduction, description of localities, preliminary faunal lists, pt. 1 of A survey of various late Cenozoic vertebrate faunas of the Panhandle of Texas: Calif. Univ. Pubs. Geol. Sci., v. 31, no. 2, p. iv, 27–49

Judson, S. S., Jr., 1950, Depressions of the northern portion of the southern High Plains of eastern New Mexico: Geol. Soc. America Bull., v. 61, no. 3, p. 253–274

McGrew, P. O., 1944, An early Pleistocene (Blancan) fauna from Nebraska: Field Mus. Nat. History, Geol. ser., v. 9, no. 2, p. 33–66

Patton, L. T., 1935, Some observations on the so-called "lakes" of the Llano Estacado of Texas [abs.]: Geol. Soc. America Proc. 1934, p. 451

Schultz, C. B., and Stout, T. M., 1941, Guide for a field conference on the Tertiary and Pleistocene of Nebraska: Nebr. State Mus. Spec. Pub., 51 p.

—— 1945, Pleistocene loess deposits of Nebraska, in Symposium on loess, 1944: Am. Jour. Sci., v. 243, no. 5, p. 231–244

—— 1948, Pleistocene mammals and terraces in the Great Plains, in Colbert, E. H., Editor, Pleistocene of the Great Plains (symposium): Geol. Soc. America Bull., v. 59, no. 6, p. 553–588

Taylor, D. W., 1960, Late Cenozoic molluscan faunas from the High Plains: U.S. Geol. Survey Prof. Paper 337, 94 p.

Wendorf, Fred, 1961, An interpretation of late Pleistocene environments of the Llano Estacado, in Wendorf, Fred, Editor, Paleoecology of the Llano Estacado: N. Mex. Press Mus., Ft. Burgwin Res. Center Pub., no. 1, p. 115–133

Wood, H. E., II, and others, 1941, Nomenclature and correlation of the North American continental Tertiary: Geol. Soc. America Bull., v. 52, no. 1, p. 1–48

Part II. Petrology

Composition and Origin of the Rita Blanca Varves

Douglas W. Kirkland

Mobil Research and Development Corporation, Dallas, Texas

Roger Y. Anderson

University of New Mexico, Albuquerque, New Mexico

INTRODUCTION

Three types of lithologic cycles are present in the lower part of the exposed Rita Blanca deposit. One type is much larger than the other two and consists of beds of sandstone alternating with limestone and calcareous clay (Fig. 5a). The second type of repetitious bedding is essentially an alternation of light-colored, carbonate-rich and dark-colored, carbonate-poor clay within one thick clay-limestone bed in the larger sequence (Fig. 5b, and Pl. 4). These clay and limestone units contain alternating light and dark laminae (Fig. 5c) which constitute a seasonal cycle (varve). The larger of these two types of cyclic layers are on a scale of centimeters and decimeters; the laminations (varves) are on a scale of millimeters. In this report the clay-limestone alternations on the centimeter-decimeter scale will be referred to as the *larger* or *long-term cycles;* the millimeter layers will be called varves; evidence supporting a seasonal and annual interpretation is presented in a later section.

PETROLOGY OF THE VARVES

General Description

Thin and polished sections of the laminated zone show repetitions of light- and dark-colored microlayers. These constitute lithologic cycles that are

15

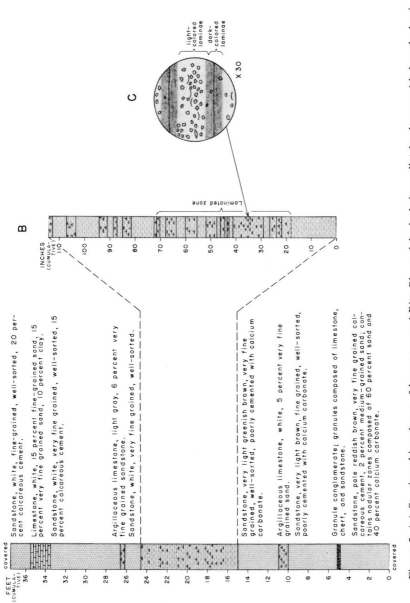

Figure 5. (a) Stratigraphic column of lower exposed Rita Blanca lake beds immediately above and below the laminated section; (b) stratigraphic column of calcareous claystone unit containing long-term cycles and laminated zone; (c) diagrammatic illustration of varve. Silt and ostracode valves occur in the light-colored layers in a matrix of calcium carbonate and clay; thin organic-rich bands occur in the middle of the dark, clay-rich layers.

repeated about 300 times per foot of section. Each couplet is interpreted as representing an annual layer of sedimentation.

The varves have an arithmetic mean thickness of 0.93 mm, a mode of about 0.70 mm, a thickness range of 0.12 to 3.40 mm, and a standard deviation of 0.59 mm. The light-colored laminae are generally from 1 to 25 times as thick as the dark. The varve thicknesses yield a right-skewed frequency distribution (Fig. 6). The dispersion is low; 75 percent of the values occur within a range of 1 mm (0.28–1.26 mm).

The color of the varves ranges from very light brownish gray to dark brownish gray. The color is related to calcium carbonate, clay, and organic matter with all three contributing to color variation (Table 7).

The varves are composed of four main constituents: clay, calcium carbonate, silt, and organic matter. The relative proportion of constituents in the light- and dark-colored laminae differs considerably (Figs. 7, 8). The composition of a particular lamina depends on its position within a long-term cycle. Varves in carbonate-rich parts of the section consist of a light-colored lamina rich in calcium carbonate and clay with minor amounts of silt, and a darker colored lamina composed of clay and organic matter. Varves in carbonate-poor parts of the section consist of a relatively light-colored lamina rich in clay with minor amounts of silt and calcium carbonate, and a darker colored lamina composed of clay and organic matter (Pl. 1; Fig. 8).

The triangular diagrams in Figure 9 show the composition and range of composition in different parts of the section. Each pair of letters, for example AA', refers to the composition of a particular varve couplet; A refers to the composition of the light-colored lamina, and A' to the composition of the dark colored lamina. Varve couplets of composition AA' occur in carbonate-rich shale and couplets of composition CC' in carbonate-poor shale. Varves of composition AA' and CC' may be thought of as representing compositional end-members with varves of intermediate composition designated arbitrarily as $B_1B'_1$ through $B_4B'_4$. The areas ABC and $A'B'C'$ in Figure 9 indicate the maximum range of compositional oscillation of the light- and dark-colored laminae, respectively.

Varves of composition between AA' and $B_1B'_1$ are very distinct and are separated by sharp and regular contacts (Pl. 1, fig. 1). Varves in the compositional range $B_1B'_1$–CC' are comparatively indistinct and are separated by contacts which are difficult to delineate accurately and which are apparently gradational (Pl. 1, fig. 3). The varve types change gradually with changing composition. These differing contact characteristics are probably due to the large compositional difference between the light- and dark-colored laminae in calcareous-rich clay sections and the slight difference in calcareous-poor clay sections (Fig. 9).

Lateral Variation in Varve Thickness

Correlation of individual varves was made over a distance of 300 yards, and varve thickness proved to be relatively constant. Plate 2 shows a correlation

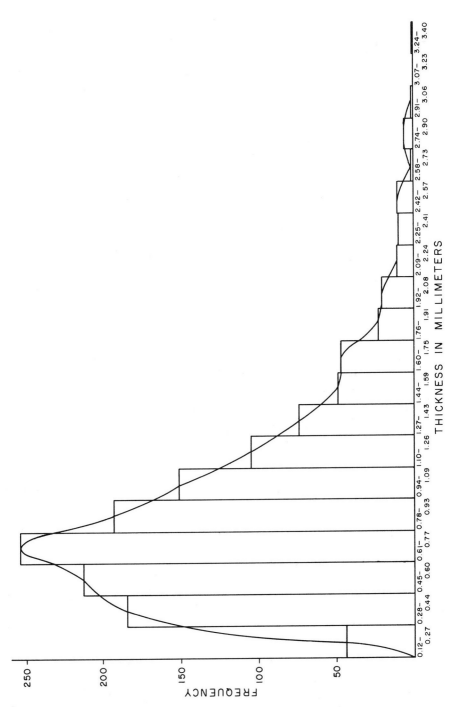

Figure 6. Frequency distribution of varve thickness.

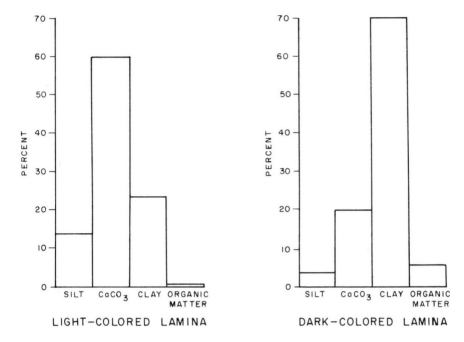

Figure 7. Approximate composition of the light- and dark-colored layers of a varve from a carbonate-rich clay section.

of 20 varves between Localities A and B (Fig. 3). The correlation is based primarily on varve thickness and also on other characteristics inherent in each individual varve or groups of varves. These characteristics include subtle color changes, exceptionally silty laminae, and abnormally thick, dark-colored laminae. The varve-thickness patterns from the two sites are similar, although the absolute thickness of individual varves differs slightly. The coefficient of correlation between the two thickness series in Plate 2 is $+ 0.90$; $n = 20$.

The correlation of laminae thickness constitutes the basis for cross-identifying glacial varves. Sauramo (1923), DeGeer (1933), and others have demonstrated cross-dating of glacial varves over distances of several hundred miles. Richter-Bernburg (1960) correlated individual laminae of anhydrite, which are probably varves, over a distance of several hundred kilometers by matching patterns of thickness variations. Anderson and Kirkland (1966) have demonstrated four examples of nonglacial varve correlation, including the Rita Blanca series.

Varve thickness in the Rita Blanca deposit generally increases from Locality A to Locality B. For example, the 20 varves in Figure 10 are 16 percent thicker at Locality B than at Locality A. The laminated zone, which includes about 1,400 varves, is 53 inches thick at Locality A and 65 inches thick at Locality B, an increase in thickness of 19 percent. Additional correlations

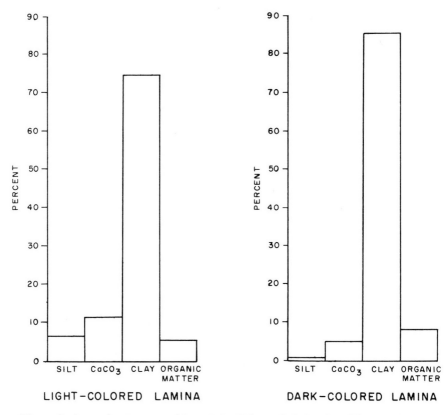

Figure 8. Approximate composition of the light- and dark-colored layers of a varve from a carbonate-poor clay section.

and varve-thickness comparisons indicate that the increased thickness of the laminated section at Locality B is due to an increase in the thickness of the majority of varves rather than the abnormal thickening of relatively few varves.

Organic Matter

Organic matter forms a small but important part of the Rita Blanca varves. Autochthonous organic matter was derived chiefly from: (1) attached vegetation which lived in the littoral zone of the lake, (2) bodies and excreta of planktonic, nektonic, and benthonic animals, and (3) bodies of phytoplankton. Fossil higher aquatic plants are rare, possibly because they contain little supporting tissue and thus decompose faster than terrestrial plants. Specimens of *Ruppia* were the only higher aquatic plants found. Midge pupae, dragonfly nymphs, other aquatic insects, and fish contributed small amounts of organic matter. The fossil flora indicates that green algae were undoubtedly abundant in the lake waters and were represented, in part, by *Botryococcus* and *Pediastrum*.

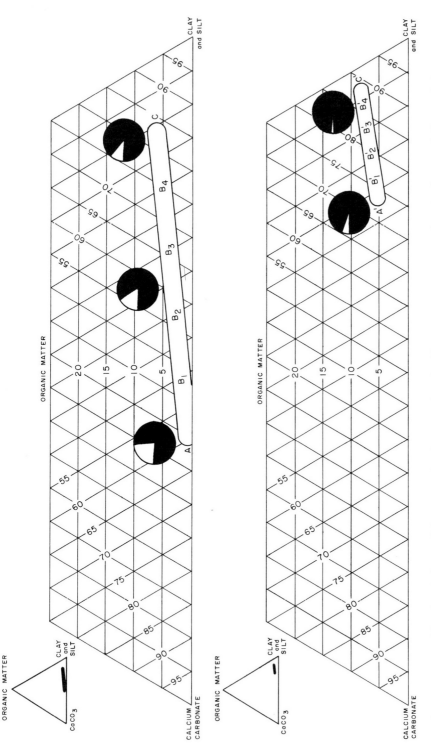

Figure 9. Compositional variation of light- and dark-colored laminae in different parts of varve series; pie diagrams indicate relative amount of silt (white). (a) Light-colored laminae above); (b) Dark-colored laminae (below).

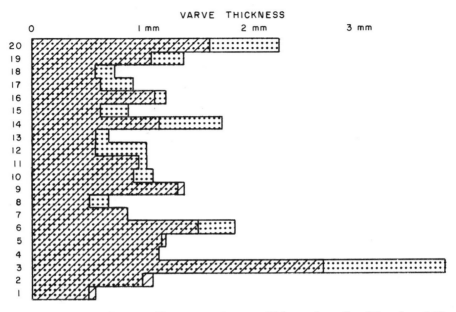

Figure 10. Superimposed histograms of varve thickness from Localities A and B (Fig. 4) showing degree of correlation; reference numbers refer to varves in Plate 2; hachured area, Locality A; dotted area, Locality B.

Semispherical organic objects about 5 to 8 microns in diameter with a botryoidal structure make up an appreciable part of the autochthonous organic matter. They are reddish brown in transmitted light. Nearly identical but slightly larger structures are associated with laminated diatomaceous sediments in Zuni Salt Lake, Catron County, New Mexico, where they are similarly concentrated in the darker layers. J. P. Bradbury (oral commun., 1965) compared the two occurrences and suggested that they resemble fungal spores of saprolegnian affinity.

The coarser allochthonous organic materials consist of nonaquatic insects and parts of terrestrial plants. Abundant plant fibers occasionally form a mat on top of light-colored laminae (Pl. 3). This organic constituent probably originated when great volumes of dead foliage, transported onto the lake, sank and became incorporated into the sediment. The plant fragments do not show preferred orientation.

A variety of terrestrial insects occur within the varved layers (Pls. 16–20). Pollen is particularly noteworthy because of its abundance and excellent preservation. A preliminary study indicates that between 2.5 and 4.5 million grains of pollen were deposited each year on 1 square foot of the lake bottom. This estimate was obtained by separating pollen from a known volume of material taken from a varve of known thickness and by counting the pollen grains in an aliquot of the final pollen residue.

Another type of allochthonous organic substance was apparently brought into the lake in solution or in a colloidal state and precipitated seasonally as thin discrete layers of a dy-type sediment. The discrete organic laminae in the clay-rich layer of varves in carbonate-rich zones are optically active. These layers are yellowish brown in plane transmitted light, have a mean thickness of about 0.08 mm, and are not pleochroic but have sharply defined parallel extinction that probably derives from relatively pure optical isomers. An interference figure could not be obtained and birefringence is low. Trager (1924, p. 309) noted that there are two types of structureless organic matter, one of which is optically active. Bradley (1931, p. 52) found, in the Green River oil shale, optically active organic matter which has a clear yellow color, lacks pleochroism, and has parallel extinction and similar layers occur in the Florissant lake sediments (McLeroy and Anderson, 1966). In carbonate-poor clay zones, optically active material appears to be dispersed throughout the dark- and light-colored laminae rather than being concentrated in discrete layers. The ultimate source of this material probably was humic matter leached from the "A" horizon of the soil (Ruttner, 1953). An extensive study of several hundred Wisconsin lakes by Birge and Juday (1934) disclosed that the average amount of dissolved organic matter in lakes studied was 12.8 mg per liter of water, that for each lake the dissolved organic matter did not show great quantitative or qualitative variation either with depth or with season, and that the dissolved organic matter was several times, often many times, greater than the total particulate organic matter in the same water. Juday (*in* Birge and Juday, 1934) did not indicate whether true solutions or colloidal solutions were involved. According to Hutchinson (1957, p. 886), the only attempt at separation by ultrafiltration appears to be that of Krogh and Lange (1932). They investigated Lake Furesø, Denmark, and found 13 times as much organic matter in solution as in colloidal suspension. In addition, they found that the dissolved organic matter was extremely stable and was hardly decomposed after months of storage either in the presence or absence of bacteria. These humic materials in solution in the lake can be precipitated mainly through encountering cations, particularly calcium (Ruttner, 1953, p. 168).

Rita Blanca Lake probably had a comparatively large amount of organic material in solution. The abundant pollen, numerous fossil leaves, and fibers (Pl. 3) attest to an adequate vegetative cover in the drainage basin. Humic material, transported into the lake by streams and ground water, would be precipitated as an organic sediment, particularly during the winter when the quantity of calcium ion was high. Preservation of the organic precipitate as a discrete band (dy) can be attributed to minimal sedimentation of calcium carbonate and coarse clastics during the quiet seasons.

An alternative explanation is that the discrete dark-colored laminae represent sedimentation of plankton which later became converted to sapropel. A classic example of nonglacial, annual stratification in Recent lake deposits is the varves formed in the deeper stagnant parts of Lake Zurich, Switzerland. Each varve consists of two laminae: (1) a light-colored lamina deposited in the summer consists predominantly of calcium carbonate with a small quantity of admixed organic matter, and (2) a dark-colored lamina deposited in the winter that consists predominantly of organic matter. The winter portion arises largely from organic sediment derived from fall and winter blooms of the blue-green algae *Oscillatoria rubescens*.

Some of the organic matter in the dark layer was contributed by *Botryococcus* and it is likely that plankton added to the organic content. Direct precipitation, however, might best account for the optical activity, the sharp contacts, and the uniformity of the discrete organic layers.

Multiple organic-rich layers occasionally occur in the carbonate-rich clay sections. They consist of two, and rarely three, organic laminae separated by a very thin parting of clay. In some cases the organic bands undulate slightly and in places are in contact. Analogous "doubling" has been observed in glacial varves (MacClintock and others, 1936, p. 355), in tree rings (Zeuner, 1952, p. 11), and in nonglacial "varves" (White, 1933, p. 567). In some cases the two layers may represent a normal sequence of organic laminae lying close together, each deposited in a particular season of successive years, but generally the "doubling" is probably due to minor and temporary modifications in the environment of sedimentation within one season. These minor features may have been caused by a few weeks of unusual weather which resulted in a brief cessation of the deposition of organic matter.

An approximate estimate of organic matter in the Rita Blanca varves was determined by loss of weight on ignition. Samples were heated to 160° C to drive off loosely bound water of hydration. They were then weighed, reheated to 340° C, and reweighed; the loss in weight ranged from about 1 to 8 percent.

The ignition technique is simple in principle but is seldom accurate as an estimator of organic matter. The method ordinarily used requires that the sample be heated to a maximum temperature of 600° C or more, but the abundance of clay and carbonate minerals in the Rita Blanca varves precludes the use of this standard technique. According to Hutchinson (1957, p. 878), "the main error in the method is due to the retention of water by the dry residue, which water cannot be removed below those temperatures at which charring occurs." Carbonates begin to evolve CO_2 between 400° C and 600° C (Galle and Runnels, 1960, p. 613). Illite, the predominant clay in the Rita Blanca varves, shows considerable water loss below 100° C, a gradual loss from 100° C to about 350° C, a relatively abrupt large loss from 350° C to about 600° C, and a gradual loss above 600° C (Grim and others, 1937, p. 825). In order to reduce the error caused by clay dehydration and calcite dissociation, an intermediate range of temperature (160° C to 340° C) was used to oxidize the organic matter.

Standard differential thermograms give a rough indication of the relative amount of organic matter present in small samples. An exothermic reaction between 180° C and 500° C is caused by organic matter. Curve A in Figure 11 is part of a differential thermogram obtained on a channel sample of five varves and run in a nitrogen atmosphere; curve B was obtained from the same sample, but run in air. The area between the curves is approximately

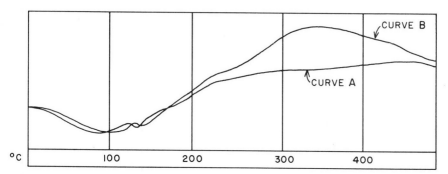

Figure 11. Differential thermograms of a Rita Blanca varve sample run in a nitrogen atmosphere (curve A) and in air (curve B).

proportional to the amount of organic matter in the sample. A comparison with Plate 5 shows the variation in organic content in the Rita Blanca samples.

The amount of organic matter was indirectly determined by using the Kjeldahl nitrogen distillation technique. The amount of extractable organic nitrogen ranged from about 0.003 percent in the light-colored high-carbonate zones to about 0.016 percent in the dark zones. If the usual correction is applied to express results in terms of percent organic matter the estimate of total organic matter is less than 0.05 percent. Analysis of individual laminae was not possible with this technique. By using a microkjeldahl apparatus, however, analyses of 5- or 20-year samples were run for the entire series. The variations with time are discussed in a later section.

The reagents tungstophosphoric and molybdophosphoric acid were used to help determine the distribution of tannin and lignin within individual varves and in the varve series (American Public Health Association, 1960). Powdered samples were treated with KOH, diluted, and subjected to the test. Extraction of tannin and lignin was not complete, and the results do not give the total amount of tannin or lignin in the samples. Also, the reagent is not always specific to tannin or lignin, and tannic acid gives a much stronger reaction than lignin.

Dark-colored low-carbonate zones contained about five times as much tannin-lignin as light-colored carbonate-rich zones (Table 2). However, no difference in the content of light- and dark-colored laminae within the zones is apparent. Tannin and lignin apparently accumulate in several ways, and the test used does not necessarily reflect the content of woody material. The relation of tannin-lignin to other parameters is also discussed in a later section (Anderson and Koopmans).

Calcium and Magnesium Carbonate

Calcium carbonate occurs primarily as microcrystalline calcite mixed in varying proportions with clay and organic matter, as ostracode valves, and, rarely, as laminae of aragonite. The calcium carbonate crystals are about

4 to 5 microns in diameter; the crystal size is not noticeably different in different microstratigraphic positions. The calcium carbonate content within the varves ranges from 5 to 60 percent. The quantity within each part of the annual couplets differs regularly, being about twice as great in the light-colored laminae as in the dark. Figure 12 shows the quantitative variation of calcium and magnesium carbonate in parts of four varves from a carbonate-rich clay zone. The amount of calcium carbonate decreases noticeably in the dark-colored laminae, whereas magnesium carbonate shows very little variation from light to dark laminae. The quantity of magnesium, expressed as magnesium carbonate, is low and apparently nearly constant throughout the varved section (Fig. 12; Appendix I).

The quantity of calcium and magnesium carbonate was determined by a titration procedure using disodium EDTA as a titrant (Banewicz and Kenner, 1952; Rainwater and Thatcher, 1960; Bisque, 1961). This method indicates the amount of calcium and magnesium ion present in a known sample, and the results are reproducible to within 1 percent. The values are reported as calcium and magnesium carbonate. Calcium carbonate determinations are probably only accurate to within 2 to 3 percent because some calcium ions were probably adsorbed on illite.

Differential thermal analysis was also used to determine the relative amount of calcium carbonate. The area under the calcium carbonate endothermic peak correlated fairly closely with the calcium carbonate value obtained by titration. The area under the illite dehydration peak between 70° C and 200° C is approximately proportional to the quantity of clay in the sample; and inasmuch as the amount of silt and organic matter is compartively low, the area is inversely related to calcium carbonate values obtained by titration.

TABLE 2. TANNIN-LIGNIN CONTENT OF LIGHT AND DARK LAMINAE FROM LIGHT AND DARK ZONES OF THE RITA BLANCA DEPOSITS. RESULTS EXPRESSED AS PERCENT TANNIC ACID

Light zone (near $T_o + 200$)		Dark zone (near $T_o + 1000$)	
Dark laminae	0.03	Dark laminae	0.15
	0.03		0.19
	0.04		0.15
	0.02		0.17
	0.04		0.17
	0.03		0.17
Average	0.03	Average	0.17
Light laminae	0.05	Light laminae	0.20
	0.04		0.19
	0.04		0.19
	0.03		0.17
	0.03		0.16
	0.03		0.19
Average	0.04	Average	0.18

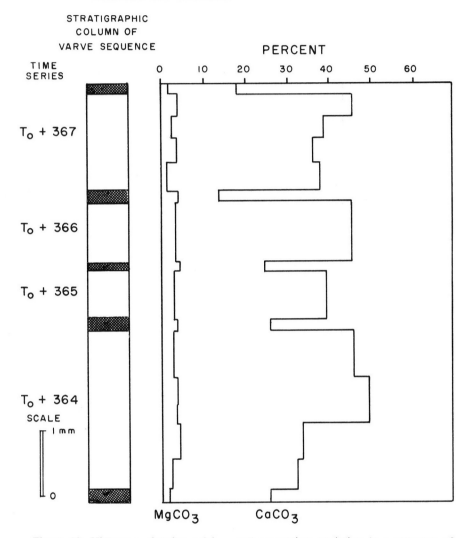

Figure 12. Histogram showing calcium and magnesium variation in a sequence of four varves between $T_0 + 364$ and $T_0 + 367$ (Appendix II); white in column represents light laminae, and dark represents dark laminae.

Two distinct laminae of white, pure aragonite occur in the varve sequence. The aragonite was identified by X-ray analysis. One lamina, about 0.2 mm in thickness, occurs at $T_0 + 158$, and the other, about 0.5 mm in thickness, occurs at $T_0 + 187$. The older aragonite band lies directly beneath a dark-colored lamina, and the younger band lies directly above a dark-colored lamina.

Escape of carbon dioxide from the surface waters of Rita Blanca Lake probably reached a maximum rate during the height of summer stagnation. This increased rate resulted primarily from an increase in the temperature of the epilimnion and from the assimilation activity of plants. During mid-summer the epilimnion was probably impoverished with respect to carbon dioxide. In reference to a typical eutrophic lake of the temperate region, Ruttner (1953, p. 65) states, "The carbon dioxide content often drops to zero and indeed may have a 'negative' value; that is, the removal of HCO_3^- is more rapid than the precipitation of calcium carbonate and a supersaturated bicarbonate-monocarbonate solution results." Nipkow (1920; 1927) found that the light-colored portion of the annual couplet in Lake Zurich consists mostly of calcite crystals that are formed in the surface water of the lake only in the summer. In Rita Blanca Lake small crystals of calcium carbonate probably formed in abundance in the zone of relatively warmer water which in summer covers the great majority of lakes in the temperate regions. These crystals, in spite of their small size, settle quite rapidly through the quiet waters of the hypolimnion onto the bottom of the lake (Bradley, 1929, p. 101; 1965, p. 1423). Fresh water in contact with the atmosphere at $4°$ C contains about twice as much CO_2 in solution as at $20°$ C. Thus in Rita Blanca Lake as water temperature increased, carbon dioxide and calcium bicarbonate in solution decreased, and calcium carbonate increased to the saturation point or became supersaturated.

Many species of algae are capable of precipitating calcium carbonate in the process of obtaining carbon dioxide for photosynthesis. Blue-green algae generally cause the precipitation of calcite rather than aragonite (Revelle and Fairbridge, 1957, p. 261). The role of algae in the formation of calcite is often of great importance. Ruttner (1953, p. 146) states, "In the lakes of the northern limestone Alps the wet weight (volume) of total plankton beneath 1 hectare amounts to from 120 to 600 kg, averaging 300 kg." Because of their great surface area, algae are especially active in removing carbon dioxide from the epilimnion.

Some of the calcium carbonate entered the lake along with the clay fraction as colloidal and larger particles in suspension in the runoff from the drainage area. The proportion of carbonate brought into the lake in suspension cannot be determined precisely, but the negligible effect that suspended carbonate had on the long-term trends of precipitated carbonate (Fig. 17b) suggests that it was relatively small. Anderson and Koopmans in a later section of this report present evidence for this conclusion.

Light-colored laminae in carbonate-rich clay zones of the Rita Blanca beds invariably contain ostracode valves. They form a small but ecologically significant portion of the total calcium carbonate.

Terrigenous Material

Clay — Illite is the principal clay mineral in the Rita Blanca sediment. Powder patterns for samples from 10 dark-colored and 7 light-colored laminae from various parts of the sequence were obtained using an iron X-ray tube with a nickel filter. Lattice spacings and intensities characteristic of illite at 10 Å, 4.90 Å, 4.45 Å, and 3.19 Å were obtained in all the samples analyzed.

In the X-ray patterns, weak lines with a lattice spacing of 7.2 Å occurred in all of the dark-colored low-carbonate layers analyzed but were absent or very weak in the light-colored high-carbonate layers. This line is indicative of kaolin, chlorite, or gypsum. Tests for sulfate ion were negative.

Grim (1953, p. 354) states, "lakes in which there is no accumulation of lime would probably show a tendency toward the development of kaolinite. In lakes where lime is accumulating, the lime would tend to block the formation of kaolinite." The negative association of carbonate and the 7.2 Å line may be related to kaolin formation during times of decreased carbonate deposition.

Silt — Angular quartz grains of silt size are often abundant in the Rita Blanca varves and are mainly confined to the light-colored laminae (Pl. 1, fig. 1). The size of the particles, based on measurements in thin sections of 200 grains in different varves, averages 0.06 mm for the longest intercepts and has a low variance (Fig. 13). The quartz silt grains are mixed with calcium carbonate crystals, illite, and ostracode valves. The proportion of silt grains is occasionally very high, and the grains may form discrete laminae. Rarely, faint alternations of silt with calcium carbonate and clay form subordinate couplets which can be distinguished easily from the primary annual couplets. Silt is more abundant in carbonate-rich clay zones than in carbonate-poor clay zones. Maximum calcium carbonate and silt deposition apparently coincided and, judging from other evidence, occurred in summer and during prolonged intervals of dry climate. The silt probably was brought into the lake by both eolian and fluvial processes.

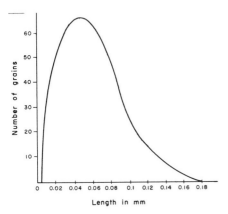

Figure 13. Frequency curve showing variation in length of silt grains in Rita Blanca varve series.

EVIDENCE FOR THE ANNUAL NATURE OF THE LAMINATIONS

The proof that a particular sedimentary bed was deposited in 1 year's time is a difficult task, and Hansen (1940) and Schneider (1945), in particular, have called for a critical attitude in regard to the probable time value of cyclic laminae. The position of insects and plants in alternating laminae of calcium carbonate and clay in an upper Miocene lake sequence near Oeningen, Germany, has been used to demonstrate annual layering or varves (Heim, 1909). Deposits of the Faulensee near Spiez, Switzerland, which was drained in 1920, contain alternating laminae of calcium carbonate and organic matter interpreted as varves by Welten (1944). The annual nature of these sediments was established in several ways, including cyclic changes in total quantity and percentage composition of pollen and diatoms. Bradley (1929, 1931) considers the Eocene Green River Formation of Colorado, Utah, and Wyoming to be a varved lacustrine sequence. A variety of fossils have been found, but their microstratigraphic position has not been used to verify the annual nature of the laminae. The diatomite and sapropel layers of varves in the Oligocene Florissant lake beds of Colorado contain different proportions of conifer and hardwood pollen (McLeroy and Anderson, 1966), but the seasonal relationships of the pollen are not known.

Dark- and light-colored laminae in the Rita Blanca lake beds form couplets which were deposited within a single year and owe their origin to seasonal change of environment. Demonstration of the varved nature is based on several independent lines of evidence and reasoning, no one of which provides absolute proof of annual nature.

Evidence Provided by Ostracodes

Varves in carbonate-rich clay zones invariably contain ostracode carapaces. The exact stratigraphic position of ostracodes within the varves has been determined by thin-section investigation and by dissection of varved slabs. These techniques have convincingly demonstrated an interesting relation; the ostracode genera *Limnocythere* and *Cyprideis* are present only in light-colored layers, whereas the genus *Candona* is found within the dark-colored layer and at the contact between the base of the dark-colored layer and the top of the light-colored layer (Fig. 14). These forms have been described by R. H. Benson elsewhere in this report.

Another ostracode that cannot be identified with certainty, and that has not been described by R. H. Benson, invariably occurs at the upper contact of the light layer. This form is uniformly about 1 mm in longest dimension and has a carapace that is dominantly composed of chitinous material. This is covered by a thin layer of calcium carbonate which bears the coarsely punctate surface ornamentation that is characteristic of many ostracodes. The calcium carbonate layer does not extend to the margin of the carapace, but leaves a rim of chitinous material that encircles the valve. There is a strong median sulcus that divides the form into equal broad prominant swellings (Pl. 24, figs. 1, 3). The form has an affinity to several genera but may be most closely related to *Ilyocypris*. This unknown ostracode has one dominant size, and there is no evidence of juvenile forms or molt stages. This suggests that it may have been seasonally introduced to the site of deposition and may not have lived *in situ*. It is commonly associated with finely divided and filamentous plant debris but not with coarse fragments.

Many species of ostracodes exhibit definite seasonal periodicity (Ferguson, 1944; Hoff, 1942) which supports a seasonal and annual interpretation for the Rita Blanca laminae. Egg development is usually suspended during the

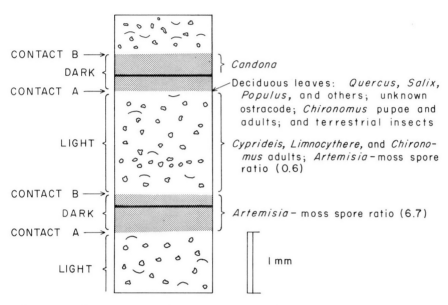

Figure 14. Diagram of Rita Blanca varves perpendicular to bedding showing position of lower (A) and upper (B) contacts of winter and summer laminae and associated microstratigraphic position of fossils.

cold months (Pennak, 1953, p. 414), and most species have a spring and summer growth period. Furthermore, Pennak (p. 415) relates that many species of *Candona* can be collected only in the spring, while only a few species can be collected in the autumn. R. H. Benson, in this report, gives further information on the seasonal population habits of the ostracodes in the Rita Blanca deposits.

Evidence Provided by Leaves

Many excellently preserved fossil leaves occur within the Rita Blanca varves. About half of the flora consists of *Quercus gambelii* and *Q. stellata*. Leaves of *Salix exigua, S. bebbiana?,* and *Populus deltoides?* are also present. The leaves are almost always unbroken and well preserved, which suggests that the time interval from shedding until deposition was short. The stratigraphic position of leaves within the varves, with only one exception, is at or near the base of the dark layer (Fig. 14). Most of the leaves occur precisely at the contact, but a few occur a fraction of a millimeter above the contact within the dark-colored laminae.

The autumnal shedding of leaves by dicotyledonous trees in temperate climates is a familiar phenomenon. The species of *Quercus* and *Salix* represented by leaves within the varves are deciduous and lose their leaves in the fall. In some oaks, dead leaves remain on trees well into winter or even into the spring.

Evidence Provided by Chironomidae (Midges)

The most common insects within the varve series are Chironomidae. Meta-morphosis is complete in this family of Diptera; an insect passes in its growth from egg through the larva and pupa to the adult. Adult midges are fairly common in the varve sequence. Midge pupae, especially of the genus *Chironomus,* are abundant, some bedding planes containing more than 40 individuals per square inch. Fossil larvae, however, were not observed ex-cept for a single head capsule. (*See* article by J. E. Sublette in this report.)

Midge pupae were observed at the contact between the top of the light-and the base of the dark-colored layer in 15 varves. No pupae were found in other stratigraphic positions. One individual pupa found had begun to shed its skin before emerging as an adult, but had died before completing this process (Pl. 15, fig. 2). In 19 cases, adult midges were found at the base of the dark layer (at the contact between the two layers), and in 6 cases, adults were found at various positions within the light-colored layer.

The larval stages pupate in their larval tunnels or cases, usually in shallow water, and come to the surface of the water only slightly before the adults hatch (Wirth and Stone, 1956, p. 407). Pupae ordinarily swim actively near the surface of the lake for less than 24 hours (J. E. Sublette, oral commun., 1962). Midge pupae are by far the most abundant type of fossil insect in the laminated sequence. Numerous midge pupae have been observed on bedding planes of laminated strata from the Florissant lake deposits of Colorado, and their death has been attributed to volcanic ash falls. A more probable answer has been provided by J. E. Sublette (oral commun., 1962) based on observations of recent lakes in Oklahoma and Texas. In spring or autumn, a warm spell may initiate metamorphosis in larvae which then pupate and swim to the surface. A decrease in temperature of the surface water at this stage will cause a mass mortality of the pupae, some in a state of ecdysis, before the adults can emerge. Wind may then blow the pupae into deeper parts of the lake where they may decompose, be eaten by fish, or sink and become incorporated in bottom sediments. Based on stratigraphic position of the midge pupae, the bottom of the dark-colored layer probably repre-sents spring or fall. In either case, seasonal variation of the environment is indicated, which attests to the annual nature of the sedimentary layers.

In temperate climates, adult midges emerge during the warmer months; therefore, the well-preserved midges in the light-colored layers were prob-ably deposited during the spring, summer, or early fall. The abundance of adult midges at the top of the light-colored layer may have been partly due to increased mortality in association with decreased rate of sedimentation. The laminated slabs have a tendency to split at a contact rather than within the dark-or light-colored layers. Thus, even though many adult midges might be present within the light-colored layers, they would not be as readily ob-served as those on a contact.

It should be pointed out that the tendency to split along contacts does not in the least affect the seasonal interpretations, since the varved strata seem to split as readily on one contact as another. For example, leaves, midge pupae and adults, and the unidentified ostracode are found at contact A (Fig. 14), but seldom or never at contact B, although equally as many bedding faces at contact B were searched for fossils.

Evidence Provided by Pollen

The ratio of *Artemisia* (sagebrush) pollen to total pollen is different in light- and dark-colored laminae. In a preliminary study, pollen was separated from five dark-colored and four light-colored laminae. The relative proportion of *Artemisia* in the light laminae averaged 69 percent and in the dark laminae 48 percent. In a more detailed study, pollen was separated from three dark- and three adjacent light-colored laminae from a calcium carbonate-rich shale zone in another part of the section; *Artemisia* formed an average of 54 percent of the total pollen flora in the light-colored laminae and 41 percent in the dark-colored laminae. The remaining pollen percentages were made up largely of Gramineae, *Quercus,* Chenopodiaceae-Amaranthaceae, Compositae, Coniferales, and other forms discussed by Harbour in this report. A small spore of unknown genus, but probably with moss affinities, occurs in relatively great abundance in dark-colored laminae; the ratio between *Artemisia* pollen and moss? spores in light and dark laminae differs considerably (Table 3).

Artemisia is usually wind pollinated in summer and early fall. An *Artemisia* pollen grain with a diameter of 25 microns and a specific gravity of 1.35 would sink in fresh water, according to Stokes' law, at a rate of about 0.1 mm per second in quiet water at 20° C. The rate of sinking would have been relatively rapid and the majority of sagebrush pollen transported into the epilimnion may have been deposited on the lake bottom within a month after the pollen was shed. The upper part of a lake maintains a state of continuous mixing action (Ruttner, 1953, p. 102). Vertical currents to some extent tend to counterbalance sinking, and some pollen would undoubtedly have remained suspended in the water until late fall or early winter.

Evidence Provided by Carbon and Oxygen Isotopes

Carbon and oxygen isotope analyses of nine light and nine dark layers were run with consistent results. The carbon in the carbonate associated with the dark-colored layers was enriched in C^{12}. Enrichment of O^{16} in the light-colored layers can best be explained by a greatly increased rate of evaporation, which suggests that the carbonate deposited in these laminae was precipitated in the summer. A detailed discussion of the isotope analyses is found in the article in this report by J. N. Weber.

Table 3. Pollen and Spore Variation in Light- and Dark-colored Laminae from Rita Blanca Varve Series; See Appendix II for Time Series

Laminae examined	Percent of *Artemisia* in total pollen					Average
(Preliminary study)						
Time (years)	$T_o + \times$	$T_o + (\times + 1)$	$T_o + (\times + 2)$	$T_o + (\times + 3)$	$T_o + (\times + 4)$	
Light-colored laminae	65	72	66	73		69
Dark-colored laminae	48	57	48	40	47	48
Time (years)	$T_o + 340$	$T_o + 342$	$T_o + 346$			
Light-colored laminae	52	55	56			54
Dark-colored laminae	36	48	39			41
	Ratio *Artemisia* pollen to moss spores					
Time (years)	$T_o + 340$	$T_o + 342$	$T_o + 346$			
Light-colored laminae	3.3	14.4	2.5			
Dark-colored laminae	0.7	0.7	0.3			

TABLE 4. CHARACTERISTICS OF VARVES OF RECENT NONGLACIAL LAKES

Reference	Lake	Lithology and season of deposition of light-colored laminae	Lithology and season of deposition of dark-colored laminae	Average varve thickness	Depth of formation within lake	Comments
Nipkow, 1920, 1927	Zurich, Switzerland	Calcium carbonate, summer	Organic matter, winter	3 mm	Below 295 feet	Varves have formed since 1896 due to human eutrophication
Perfiliev, 1927	Saki, northern Crimea, Russia	Fine-grained sand or calcium sulfate, summer	Organic matter, spring (peak production)	1.3 mm	..	Saline lake
Welten, 1944	Faulensee, Switzerland	Calcium carbonate, summer	Organic matter, winter	0.8 mm	..	Drained in 1920
Journaux, 1952	Selune, France	Diatoms, summer	Clay and organic matter, winter	3.4–4.1 mm	Below 39 feet	Varves formed behind dam; lake drained in 1952
Whittaker, 1922	McKay, Ottawa, Canada	Calcium carbonate, spring	Organic matter, summer and fall	0.43 mm	About 30 feet	Seasonal designation not definite; laminae possibly due to human eutrophication
Eggleton, 1931	Third Sister, Michigan	Clay, spring	Organic matter, summer, fall, and winter	15–30 mm	About 16 feet	Laminae possibly due to human eutrophication

Application of the Principle of Uniformitarianism

Varves are forming today in modern nonglacial lakes. Table 4 lists the salient features of varves of some Recent nonglacial lakes which have been described in the literature. Annual laminations in Recent lakes are notably rare. These lakes are all located within the north temperate zone, and, with the exception of Saki Lake, all within western Europe and northeastern North America, the two major areas of limnological investigation. As detailed limnological studies are undertaken outside of these areas, and especially in lower latitudes, more examples of varved sediments will probably be found. Chilingar (1956) states that the large lakes of semi-arid regions of Russia often exhibit distinct microlayering which reflects seasonal fluctuations, and Shostakovich (1931) reports that August Thieneman found sharply defined varves in the bottom deposits of lakes in Java, Sumatra, and Bali.

Although a great deal is unknown or poorly known about sedimentation in the lakes listed in Table 4, the laminated sediments observed in them have been a result of seasonal variation in sedimentation. These examples of lacustrine sediments with alternating organic-rich and organic-poor laminae are analogous to the Rita Blanca laminated strata, and, applying the principle of uniformitarianism, a varve interpretation for the Rita Blanca laminae is reasonable.

Consideration of Alternate Hypotheses

The laminations were undoubtedly caused by variations in the type and quantity of sediments reaching the site of deposition. Conceivably, the variation might be the result of differential settling from storm-caused turbidity currents. Assuming that a storm resulted in an influx of silt, organic matter, and clay from streams into the lake, this flood of sediment-laden water, being heavier than the lake water, would flow along the bottom into deeper parts of the basin. The included materials of differing size and weight would sink at different rates, and, finally, a stratification would result in which the lower layer would consist of silt particles and the upper layer of clay and organic matter. An objection to this proposed origin is evident. The calcium carbonate content in lighter colored laminae is often greater than 50 percent, and thin-section studies show that ostracode valves constitute less than 15 percent of this value. A light-colored layer 1 mm thick, consisting of 50 percent calcium carbonate, and having lateral uniformity of lithology, would contain about 4,000 tons of calcium carbonate per square mile of lake bottom. The cross-spectrum analysis of clay and calcium carbonate by Anderson and Koopmans in this report shows that much of this carbonate precipitated directly in the lake and that only part of it was introduced with the clay.

Turbidity currents, on the other hand, may have developed in a different manner. If one assumes that the laminae formed in a part of the lake adjacent to a shallower area whose deposits of silt, clay, calcium carbonate, and organic matter were periodically thrown into suspension by storm waves or during overturn, then the sediment-laden water that resulted might flow as a turbidity current into deeper parts of the lake, settle at different rates, and result in laminae of relatively coarse and less coarse material.

Several lines of fossil evidence suggest that the laminae in the Rita Blanca deposit were not formed in this manner. The invariant microstratigraphic position of valves of the ostracodes *Limnocythere, Candona,* and *Cyprideis;* the unidentified ostracode; deciduous leaves; *Artemisia* pollen; and moss spores cannot be accounted for by gravity settling.

Graded bedding, a primary characteristic of turbidity deposition, is not present in the Rita Blanca laminae. The coarser sediment fraction, rather than being found at the base of light-colored laminae, often occurs near the middle.

Individual laminae can be correlated over a distance of 300 yards with little change in thickness or lithologic character. It seems unlikely that this degree of lateral uniformity would exist if directional turbidity currents were responsible for introducing the material.

The dark-colored laminae also contain several stratigraphic features which cannot be explained easily if these laminae are considered to be a product of differential settling from a rather sudden influx of various constituents. Thin sections reveal that organic matter is often concentrated in the middle of dark-colored laminae and is underlain and overlain by clay. In addition, the organic matter sometimes occurs in two and rarely three bands separated by thin layers of clay. These observations can best be explained if they are considered to be variations in the supply of constituents throughout a season or longer period of time.

Seasonal Associations of Laminae

The microstratigraphic positions of the various fossils found in association with the laminae are summarized in Figure 14. The enrichment of O^{18}, the increased frequency of summer- and fall-flowering *Artemisia* pollen, the abundance of midges, the occurrence of late spring and summer blooming *Limnocythere* and *Cyprideis,* and the increased precipitation of calcium carbonate all suggest that the light-colored layers represent summer or warm-season deposition. The occurrence of deciduous leaves at the top of the light-colored layer or slightly within the overlying dark-colored layer suggests that the dark-colored layer represents winter deposition. The rate of deposition in the winter, however, may have been very slow, particularly if the lake had an ice cover. It is possible, therefore, that the dark layer might also represent early spring deposition before the late spring and summer bloom climax of *Limnocythere* and *Cyprideis.* This interpretation would best account for the occurrence of *Candona,* which has an early spring bloom climax, within the dark layers. *Candona* is known to burrow into the substratum during its scavenging for food, but the near absence of articulated carapaces suggests that these littoral forms were transported into the deeper part of the lake and were entrapped during spring sedimentation.

PETROLOGY OF THE LARGER CYCLES

Larger lithologic cycles are superimposed on the varves. In outcrop these cycles are strikingly displayed by color changes (Pl. 4). The lighter colored beds are relatively richer in calcium carbonate and poorer in organic matter and clay than the darker beds. The varves provide a calibration tool for determining the time involved in the formation of the larger cycles and for studying the associated change in the various components. The stratigraphically lowest varve in the time series has been arbitrarily given a time value of T_o; the highest varve has a time value of $T_o + 1,401$ years (Appendix II).

Eight different parameters of long-term change were measured on an alternating 5-year or continuous 20-year sampling interval (Appendix I). These include thickness, color index, calcium carbonate content, clay content, kjeldahl nitrogen percentage, tannin-lignin percentage, O^{18}/O^{16}, and C^{13}/C^{12}. In addition, magnesium carbonate analyses were obtained for a number of samples and differential thermal analysis curves have been plotted for the complete time-series.

The average thickness of 5-varve groups is plotted against time in Figure 15a. Figure 15b is a similar diagram in which the 5-varve groups have been further smoothed according to the formula $(A + 2B + C)/4$. Abnormally thick varves caused by silt influx or the abnormally thin varves caused by misinterpretation of "doubles" might lead to an erroneous interpretation of variation with time. Therefore, Figure 15c was constructed as was Figure 15b but using limiting values of one-half standard deviation above the mean and one standard deviation below the mean (1.23 mm and 0.33 mm respectively). The result differs little from the nonlimited curve. When considered over a short term, that is, 5 to 100 years, the variation in varve thickness is relatively large. However, when considered over a long term, that is, 1,400 years, the variation in varve thickness is remarkably constant. A harmonic analysis of the thickness changes has been done, and this, together with several other statistical aspects of varve variation, is discussed in the section of this report by Anderson and Koopmans.

The color of powdered varve samples ranges from very light brownish gray to dark brownish gray. Finely powdered samples of the sample intervals were placed in 2-inch lengths of 0.25-inch diameter glass tubing, and both ends were blocked with cotton. The samples were arranged in sequence from lightest to darkest, using sunlight and a dark background. The lightest colored sample was given a color-index value of 1, the next, 2, and so on, to the darkest sample which had an index of 113. The change in color between samples with a color index of x and $x + 1$ is extremely small, yet in general the samples were ranked with ease. Judd (1961, p. 307) estimates that there are 100 million distinguishable different color stimuli. Figure 16b represents the variation of color with time. The article in this report by Anderson and Koopmans shows how calcium carbonate, clay, and organic matter all have an influence on color variation.

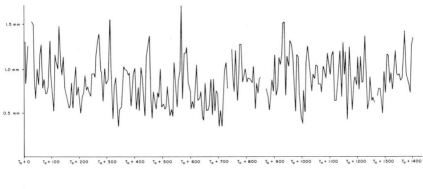

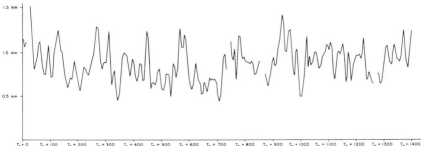

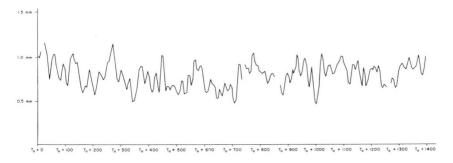

Figure 15. Curves showing variation of varve thickness with time. (a) Curve constructed by plotting the average thickness of 5 varves. (b) Curve constructed by plotting the average thickness of 5 varves (values not limited); varve groups smoothed by the formula: average thickness $= (A + 2B + C)/4$. (c) Curve constructed by plotting the average thickness of 5 varves limited by values of 1.23 mm and 0.33 mm; varve groups smoothed by the formula: average thickness $= (A + 2B + C)/4$.

The quantity of calcium carbonate in 5- and 20-year samples was determined by titration using Na_2EDTA and by differential thermal analysis, as previously described. The results are plotted in Figure 16a as the percent variation of calcium carbonate with time.

The availability of annual thickness data makes it possible to calculate the total amount of the different components deposited in a unit of time. The product of the percent $CaCO_3$ and the thickness of the 5- or 20-year sample

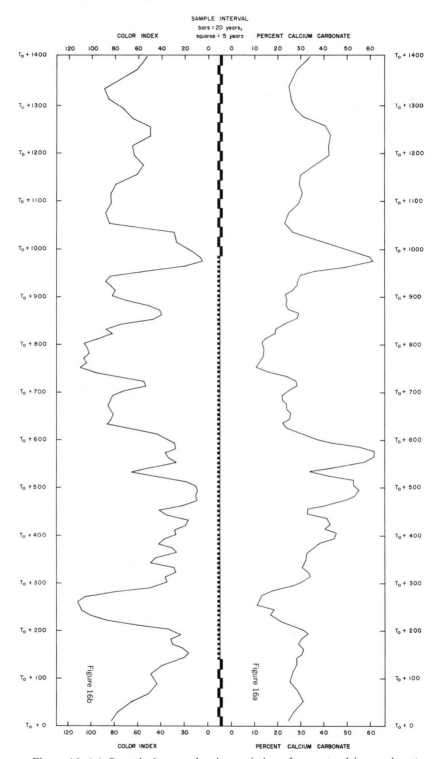

Figure 16. (a) Smoothed curve showing variation of percent calcium carbonate with time. (b) Smoothed curve showing variation of color index with time. 120 = dark brownish gray, 1 = light brownish gray. (*See* text, p. 38.)

for which the determination was made is a measure of the quantity of $CaCO_3$ deposited in that time interval; in this case expressed as thickness (mm) units. This method of evaluating compositional changes in time is more meaningful than relying on relative values. For example, 20 percent calcium carbonate in a thick unit may actually indicate a higher rate of carbonate deposition than 40 percent $CaCO_3$ in a thinner unit. The rate of $CaCO_3$ deposition was determined in this manner (Fig. 17b).

The rate of clay deposition (Fig. 17a) was also computed. The relative (percent) clay content in a 5-year sample is approximately the complement of the $CaCO_3$ percentage, since silt and organic matter constitute only a small part of the total. Hence, the rate of clay deposition was obtained by subtracting the rate of $CaCO_3$ deposition from the thickness of the varve unit used. When the rate of clay deposition increases, the amount of $CaCO_3$ deposited does not necessarily decrease but might also increase.

The resulting curves for "absolute" $CaCO_3$ and clay show an inverse relationship in their long-term variations (Fig. 17). (*See also* the statistical paper by Anderson and Koopmans in this report.) Previously, the thickness curve was stated to be relatively constant throughout the 1,400-year series. However, clay and calcium carbonate deposition both exhibit considerable variability. The inverse behavior of the accumulation rates of these two dominant components results in a relatively constant thickness for the varve series.

The magnesium carbonate content in the Rita Blanca varves shows little variation with time (Appendix I). The amount of magnesium carbonate in 5-year samples was determined by titration using Na_2EDTA. In 56 5-year samples between $T_o + 210$ and $T_o + 815$, the range was 1 to 4 percent, and the average about 2.5 percent. No obvious correlation between the quantity of magnesium carbonate and the quantity of calcium carbonate is evident.

The relative (percent) values obtained for tannin-lignin and organic nitrogen by microkjeldahl distillation were also converted to "absolute" values (Fig. 18). These two curves generally parallel each other in the interval between $T_o + 300$ and $T_o + 1,100$ years, but there is less agreement at the beginning and end of the series. The organic curves also exhibit correlation with clay, $CaCO_3$ and color as discussed in the paper by Anderson and Koopmans in this report.

The O^{16}/O^{18} and C^{12}/C^{13} ratios for the same samples were determined by Weber. The ratios of both isotopes are consistently different for light and dark laminae, but the same effect does not hold for the long term variations. The significance of the long-term changes in isotope ratios is considered by Weber in another section of this report.

Differential thermal analysis curves of 5- and 20-year spot and channel samples over 1,401 years are shown in Plate 5. The curves graphically indicate the cyclic changes in varve lithology with time. Each curve shows transformations in which heat is taken up or given off. The relative quantity of constituents causing a particular characterization of the differential thermal curve is roughly proportional to the area under the curve (Smothers and others, 1951, p. 1). In the case of the Rita Blanca samples, the reactions

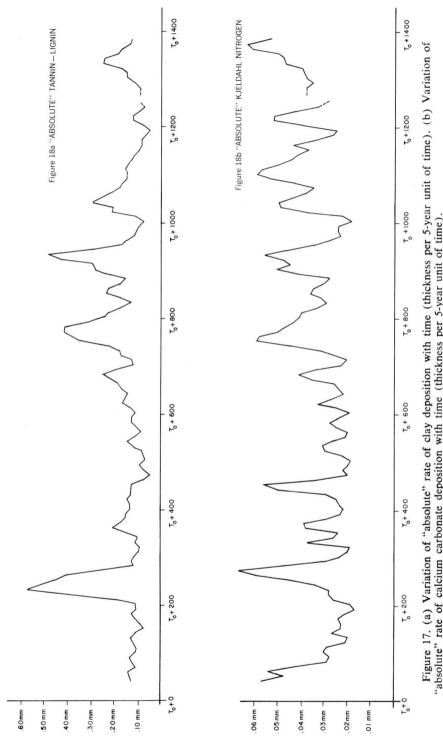

Figure 17. (a) Variation of "absolute" rate of clay deposition with time (thickness per 5-year unit of time). (b) Variation of "absolute" rate of calcium carbonate deposition with time (thickness per 5-year unit of time).

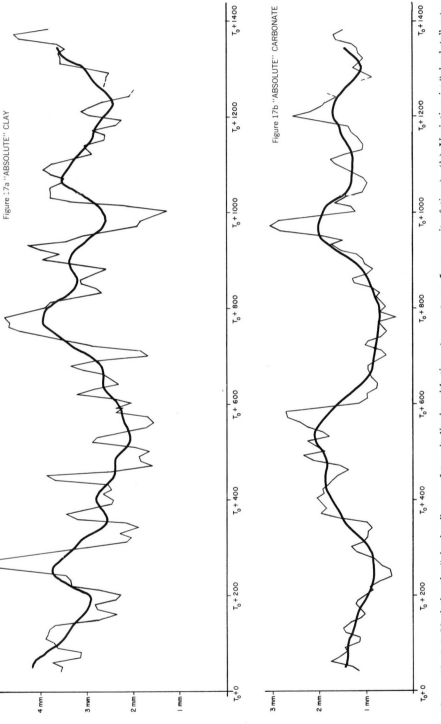

Figure 7a "ABSOLUTE" CLAY

Figure 17b "ABSOLUTE" CARBONATE

Figure 18. (a) Variation in "absolute" rate of tannin-lignin with time (amount per 5-year unit of time). (b) Variation in "absolute" rate of organic nitrogen (Kjeldahl nitrogen) accumulation with time (amount per 5-year unit of time).

are mainly the dehydration of illite, the burning off of organic material, and the decarbonation of carbonates. Illite and calcium carbonate yield the most characteristic deflections. Endothermic deflections between 70° C and 200° C are caused by the loss of interlayer water. The broad exothermic curve between about 200° C and 530° C is caused largely by the oxidation of organic matter (Fig. 11). A small, broad endothermic peak between 530° C and 600° C, evident in most of the thermograms in Plate 5, is caused by illite. A third endothermal peak, also caused by illite, occurs within the range of 780° C and 850° C and is well displayed by samples low in calcium carbonate. A high-temperature exothermic peak between 850° C and 900° C is apparently caused by illite (Grim, 1953, p. 235). The calcium carbonate endothermic peak occurs within the range 840° C to 925° C. Samples with greater amounts of calcium have higher dissociation temperatures, probably because a large quantity of carbon dioxide quickly evolves and affects the equilibrium. The cause for the double dehydration peaks between 70° C and 200° C (which are particularly evident in differential thermogram 101, Pl. 5) is not known, nor is the cause known for the small, sharp endothermic peak just above the normal calcium carbonate deflection, which is best expressed in differential thermogram 103, Plate 5.

A comparison of the seasonal and long-term petrologic changes in the varve series shows that the various parameters of change were responding together to both the annual or seasonal variations and to the more irregular trends of several hundred years. Times of increased calcium carbonate precipitation, ostracode production, and silt influx are associated at both levels of change. Times of increased illite influx, authigenic kaolin? formation, organic accumulation, and production of certain aquatic insects are also associated on an annual and long-term basis.

REFERENCES CITED

American Public Health Association, Inc., 1960, Standard methods for the examination of water and waste water including bottom sediments and sludges: New York, Am. Pub. Health Assoc., Inc., 626 p.

Anderson, R. Y., and Kirkland, D. W., 1966, Intra-basin varve correlation: Geol. Soc. America Bull., v. 77, p. 241–255

Banewicz, J. T., and Kenner, C. T., 1952, Determination of calcium and magnesium in limestones and dolomites: Anal. Chemistry, v. 24, p. 1186

Birge, E. A., and Juday, C., 1934, Particulate and dissolved organic matter in inland lakes: Ecol. Mon., v. 4, p. 440–474

Bisque, R. E., 1961, Analysis of carbonate rocks for calcium, magnesium, iron, and aluminum with EDTA: Jour. Sed. Petrology, v. 31, no. 1, p. 113–122

Bradley, W. H., 1929, The varves and climate of the Green River Epoch: U.S. Geol. Survey Prof. Paper 154, p. 87–110

—— 1931, Origin and microfossils of the oil shale of the Green River Formation of Colorado and Utah: U.S. Geol. Survey Prof. Paper 168, 58 p.

—— 1965, Vertical density currents: Science, v. 150, p. 1423–1428

Chilingar, G. V., 1956, Sediments of Sevan Lake, Armenian SSR: Compass, v. 33, no. 3, p. 275–276

DeGeer, Gerard, 1933, International geo-chronology; its origin and scope: Pan-Am. Geology, v. 60, no. 5, p. 333–347

Eggleton, F. E., 1931, A limnological study of the profundal bottom fauna of certain fresh-water lakes: Ecol. Mon., v. 1, no. 3, p. 231–331

Ferguson, E., Jr., 1944, Studies of the seasonal life history of three species of freshwater Ostracoda: Am. Midland Naturalist, v. 32, p. 713–727

Galle, O. K., and Runnels, R. T., 1960, Determination of CO_2 in carbonate rocks by controlled loss on ignition: Jour. Sed. Petrology, v. 30, no. 4, p. 613–618

Grim, R. E., 1953, Clay mineralogy: New York, McGraw-Hill, 384 p.

Grim, R. E., Bray, R. H., and Bradley, W. F., 1937, The mica in argillaceous sediments: Am. Mineralogist, v. 22, no. 7, p. 813–829

Hansen, S., 1940, Varvighed i danske og skaanske senglaciale Aflejringer [Varves in Danish and Scanian late-glacial deposits]: Copenhagen, Danm, Geol. Unders., 478 p.

Heim, A., 1909, Einige Gedanken über Schichtung: Verteljahrssachr. naturf. Gesell. Zürich, p. 330–342

Hoff, C. C., 1942, The ostracods of Illinois: Univ. Ill. Biol. Mon. 19, 196 p.

Hutchinson, G. E., 1957, A treatise on limnology: New York, John Wiley and Sons, 1015 p.

Journaux, Andre, 1952, Depot actuel de varves lacustres en Normandie: Acad. Sci. [Paris], Comptes rendus, v. 235, no. 25, p. 1669–1672

Judd, D. B., 1961, National Bureau of Standards, Washington, D.C.: The Encyclopedia Americana, New York, Chicago, Washington, D.C., Americana Corporation, v. 7, p. 307

Krogh, A., and Lange, E., 1932, Quantitative Untersuchungen über Plankton, Kolloide und gelöste organische und anorganische Substanzen in dem Füresee: Internatl. Rev. Hydrobiology, v. 26, p. 20–53

MacClintock, Paul, Barbour, E. H., Schultz, C. B., and Lugn, A. L., 1936, A Pleistocene lake in the White River Valley: Am. Naturalist, v. 70, no. 729, p. 346–360

McLeroy, C. A., and Anderson, R. Y., 1966, Laminations of the Oligocene Florissant lake deposits, Colorado: Geol. Soc. America Bull., v. 77, p. 605–618

Nipkow, H. F., 1920, Vorläufige Mitteilungen über Untersuchungen des Schlammabsatzes im Zürichsee: Zeitschr. Hydrologie, v. 1, p. 100–122

—— 1927, Über das Verhalten der Skellete planktonischer Kiselalgen im geschichteten Tiefenschlamm des Zürich und Baldeggersees: Rev. Hydrobiologie, 4th Ann., p. 71–120

Pennak, R. W., 1953, Fresh-water invertebrates of the United States: New York, Ronald Press, 796 p.

Perfiliev, B. V., 1927, Ten years of Soviet science: Moscow, p. 402–403

Rainwater, F. H., and Thatcher, L. L., 1960, Methods for collection and analysis of water samples: U.S. Geol. Survey Water-Supply Paper 1454, 301 p.

Revelle, Roger, and Fairbridge, Rhodes, 1957, Carbonates and carbon dioxide, in Hedgepeth, J. W., Editor, Treatise on marine ecology and paleoecology: Geol. Soc. America Mem. 67, v. 1, p. 238–296

Ruttner, Franz, 1953, Fundamentals of limnology: Canada, Univ. Toronto Press, 242 p.

Sauramo, Matti, 1923, Studies on the Quaternary varve sediments in southern Finland: Helsinki, Comm. Geologique de Finlande Bull. no. 60

Schneider, J. M., 1945, Meterologisches zu Weltens Faulenseesediment und schwedisch-finnischen Warwen: Verh. Schweizer Naturf. Gesell., p. 125–126

Shostakovich, V. B., 1931, Die Bedeutung der Untersuchung der Bodenablagerungen der Seen fur einige Fragen der Geophysik: Internat. Vervand Theor. Angew. Limnol. Verh. Stuttgart, v. 5, p. 307–317

Smothers, W. J., Chiang, Yao, and Wilson, Alan, 1951, Bibliography of differential thermalanalysis: Ark. Univ. Res. Ser., no. 21, 44 p.

Trager, E. A., 1924, Kerogen and its relation to the origin of oil: Am. Assoc. Petroleum Geologists Bull., v. 8, no. 3, p. 301–311

von Richter-Bernburg, G., 1960, Zeitmessung geologischer vorgange nach warvenkorrelationen im Zechstein: Geol. Rundschau, v. 49, pt. 1, p. 132–148

Welten, Max, 1944, Pollenanalytische, stratigraphische, und geochronologische Untersuchungen aus dem Faulenseemoos bei Spiez: Geobot. Inst. Rubel Veröff (Zürich), v. 21, p. 1–201

White, David, 1933, Informal communications: Washington Acad. Sci. Jour., v. 23, p. 567–568

Whittaker, E. J., 1922, Bottom deposits of McKay Lake, Ottawa (Ontario): Royal Soc. Canada, Proc. and Trans., 3d ser., v. 16, sec. 4, p. 141–157

Wirth, W. W., and Stone, Alan, 1956, Aquatic diptera, *in* Unsinger, R. L., *Editor,* Aquatic insects of California: Berkeley and Los Angeles, Univ. Calif. Press, p. 372–482

Zeuner, F. E., 1952, Dating the past: London, Methuen and Co., 495 p.

Carbon and Oxygen Isotopic Composition of Carbonate Material in the Rita Blanca Varves

Jon N. Weber

Pennsylvania State University, University Park, Pennsylvania

INTRODUCTION

The interpretation of C^{13}/C^{12} and O^{18}/O^{16} ratios of the carbonate material deposited in lacustrine environments may involve considerable difficulties because of the many factors which may affect the carbon and oxygen isotopic composition. While the sense or direction of the various effects are known, the magnitude and importance of some of these factors have yet to be determined. However, several factors affecting isotope ratios may be removed from consideration if their effect is either negligible or if operation of the factors can be shown to be highly improbable or in conflict with well-established geological evidence.

EXPERIMENTAL METHODS

Samples of varved lake sediment, normally representing either 20- or 5-year intervals, were crushed to 80-mesh particle size prior to heating for 20 minutes at 420° C in flowing helium — a treatment designed to remove volatile organic compounds which might interfere with mass spectrometric analysis. The residue was treated with excess anhydrous orthophosphoric acid under vacuum, and carbon dioxide was evolved in the reaction over a 24-hour period. The carbon dioxide was purified by the removal of acid and water vapor, and was analyzed isotopically with a 6-inch, 60° sector mass spectrometer, with an isotope ratio recording system similar to that described by McKinney and others (1950), in which the isotopic ratio of the samples gas is compared with that of a carbon dioxide standard gas every 1.25 minutes using an automatic recycling timing device to operate the solenoid gas valves permitting carbon dioxide to enter the mass spectrometer tube. Isotope ratios are expressed as the difference in C^{13} content ($\delta\,C^{13}$, in parts per thousand, that is, permil) relative to the C^{13} content of the Chicago PDB standard CO_2 by the relationship:

$$\delta\,C^{13} = \left(\frac{C^{13}/C^{12} \text{ sample}}{C^{13}/C^{12} \text{ PDB standard}} - 1 \right) 1000$$

and are corrected for the presence of O^{17} in the gas samples, as described by Craig (1957). Because of the difficulty of sampling finely varved sediments, only relatively small samples were available, which, in the case of the low $CaCO_3$ samples, yielded quantities of carbon dioxide insufficient for analysis using conventional apparatus. To overcome this difficulty, a capillary "micropiston" was incorporated in the hardware of the mass spectrometer, which by adjustment of the mercury level in the fine tubing containing the sample carbon dioxide, permitted the measurement of isotope ratios using the normal ion beam intensity of 25 volts. Carbon dioxide samples were prepared and analyzed with a total analytical random error for $\delta\,C^{13}$ and $\delta\,O^{18}$ of less than 0.2 permil.

Data reduction, statistical processing of the data and calculation of the δ values from instrument readings were performed automatically with the aid of an IBM digital computer.

RESULTS

The carbon and oxygen isotope ratios for each individual sample, expressed in the form of δ values, are presented in Appendix I; the sampling intervals are the same as those described in the paper on petrology by Kirkland and Anderson in this report. The individual analyses are plotted against time in Plate 6.

Table 5 illustrates the consistent enrichment of C^{12} and O^{16} in the dark layer, relative to the light layer, which together constitute a varve.

Because of the relatively large difference in isotopic composition between summer and winter layers of the varve, and hence the importance of seasonal variation relative to isotope ratio changes over longer periods of time, individual analyses were grouped to obtain δ values for 40-year, 60-year, 80-year, and 100-year intervals. The results are plotted against time in Figures 19–22.

The results of linear regression and correlation analysis for various pairs of variables ($\delta\,C^{13}$, $\delta\,O^{18}$, and percentage of calcium carbonate) are reported in Table 6. Only the correlation coefficient for $\delta\,C^{13}$ against $\delta\,O^{18}$ is statistically significant at the 1 percent level of significance, indicating a close and direct relationship between these two variables. A further comparison between $\delta\,C^{13}$ and $\delta\,O^{18}$ and other parameters has been made in the paper by Anderson and Koopmans in this report.

TABLE 5. CARBON AND OXYGEN ISOTOPIC COMPOSITION OF LIGHT
AND DARK LAMINAE IN RITA BLANCA VARVES

Sample number	Type of laminae		δ C^{13}*	δ O^{18}*
1	light		−4.68	−4.12
2	light		−4.35	−3.61
3	light		−4.41	−4.04
4	light		−4.13	−3.35
5	light		−4.13	−3.34
6	light		−4.04	−3.23
7	light		−3.90	−3.41
8	light		−3.88	−2.90
9	light		−3.70	−3.00
		Average	4.14	3.44
1	dark		−4.80	−5.30
2	dark		−5.22	−5.50
3	dark		−5.13	−6.65
4	dark		−4.79	−4.62
5	dark		−4.91	−5.52
6	dark		−4.63	−4.58
7	dark		−4.54	−4.11
8	dark		−4.39	−3.45
9	dark		−4.48	−4.49
		Average	4.77	4.91

*Relative to the Chicago PDB Standard Carbon Dioxide, in permil.

TABLE 6. LINEAR REGRESSION AND CORRELATION ANALYSIS

Parameters examined	$\bar{x}$ Average variable 1	$\bar{y}$ Average variable 2	b Slope of regression line*	r Correlation coefficient	Number of samples
(1) δ C^{13} and δ O^{18}	−3.99	−4.16	1.343	.6705†	107
(2) δ C^{13} and percent CaCO$_3$	−3.99	30.76	2.33	.106	89
(3) δ O^{18} and percent CaCO$_3$	−4.16	30.76	2.055	.200	89

*$Y_x = Y + b(X - \bar{x})$
†Statistically significant at the 1 percent level of significance.

DISCUSSION OF THE RESULTS — INTERPRETATIONS

Several of the factors which might affect the isotopic composition of the lacustrine carbonates and thereby make environmental interpretations more difficult may be neglected. The reequilibration of oxygen and carbon isotopes incorporated in the calcium carbonate with carbon and oxygen isotopes present in intrastratal solutions has probably effected no detectable change in the original isotope ratios, for the sediments are fine-grained and relatively impermeable, show no obvious evidence of recrystallization, have never been deeply buried, and were deposited after about 2,000,000 years B.P. Weber and others (1965) have demonstrated that even minute variations in isotopic composition have been preserved in the Pennsylvanian-age Vanport Limestone, especially in the case of carbon.

The ratio of fresh-water limestones (C^{12} enriched) to marine limestones (C^{13} enriched) in the drainage basin containing Rita Blanca Lake probably remained unchanged during the 1,400 years of varved deposition, and the bicarbonate ions derived from these sources undoubtedly had considerable opportunity to enter into isotopic exchange reactions with organically derived carbon dioxide in the atmosphere and in both the stream and lake water.

In the next chapter, Anderson and Koopmans have shown by means of spectral analysis that the short-term variations in carbonate may correlate with clastic influx. The trends of greater than 60-70 years duration however, are apparently the result of long-term changes in precipitation within the lake. Although clastic grains of limestone are often available for wind transportation in desert areas, it is unlikely that the volume of mechanically deposited grains of limestone account for any appreciable portion of the total carbonate sediment. Their effect, therefore, on the isotopic composition of the carbonate portion of the varves may be assumed to be negligible.

Because the latitude and altitude of meteoric precipitation remained essentially unchanged over the 1,400-year period of varved deposition, the oxygen isotope ratio of the runoff reaching the influx streams probably remained relatively constant if the air mass from which the rainwater was derived had originated in approximately the same geographic area. Climatic changes, with increased evaporation of lake and stream water — and of runoff during excessively dry periods — would tend to cause a concentration of O^{18} in the water phase, and hence would influence the δO^{18} value of the carbonate forming in the lake.

The major factor controlling the C^{12}/C^{13} ratio of the carbonate sediments is the activity of organic processes taking place both within and around the lake. During periods characterized by wet or humid conditions, the C^{12}-enriched carbon dioxide supplied by plants through respiration or bacterial decay results in the formation of C^{12}-enriched carbonate by isotopic exchange with bicarbonate ions dissolved in the lake and stream water. Whether precipitated inorganically by evaporation or other means, or derived from comminuted shells of $CaCO_3$-secreting organisms, the resultant limestone would be expected to exhibit a low C^{13}/C^{12} ratio in periods of vigorous plant (and animal) activity. Moreover, under stagnant conditions in poorly circulated water, the C^{12}-enriched CO_2 produced as a result of bacterial decay of organic material would have ample time to enrich the dissolved bicarbonate in the light carbon isotope, C^{12}. The importance of the latter mechanism in influencing the δC^{13} value of the limestone has been demonstrated by Landergren (1954) in the Limbata (Ordovician) limestones of Sweden, and by Keith and Weber (1964) in a variety of limestones of all ages.

The C^{12}/C^{13} ratio differences among various species of molluscan or ostracode carbonate are normally not great, and, unless the proportion of $CaCO_3$ obtained from different species varied enormously from time to time, this variable may be neglected.

As the fractionation factor describing the distribution of oxygen isotopes between water and calcium carbonate phases varies appreciably with temperature, $CaCO_3$ deposited in warm water would tend to be enriched in O^{16} relative to $CaCO_3$ precipitated in colder environments, all other factors being constant.

Excessively dry periods with concurrent intense evaporation would result in the concentration of O^{18} in the lake and stream water because of the lower vapor pressure of H_2O^{18}. Isotopic exchange of oxygen in the liquid H_2O and dissolved HCO_3^- would lead, therefore, to O^{18} enrichment in the limestone formed at this time. Excessively wet periods, on the other hand, with increased rainfall, would result in larger quantities of stream water (enriched in O^{16} relative to lake water) reaching the lake. Although the O^{16}/O^{18} ratio of the stream water will probably vary to some extent, large changes in the volume of discharge would be expected to show an appreciable effect.

Average Isotopic Composition of Rita Blanca Carbonates

The average δC^{13} value (-3.99) of the entire 1,400-year sequence (Table 5) falls well within the range of carbon isotopic composition of lacustrine carbonates (Weber and Keith, 1962). Dispersion, represented by the standard deviation of 0.686 permil, is relatively small. The average δO^{18} value (-4.16) is somewhat high for calcium carbonate precipitated in fresh water but by no means suggests noncontinental deposition. Dispersion of the O^{18}/O^{16} ratios, expressed as the standard deviation in delta notation as 1.37 permil, is considerably greater than in the case of carbon.

Variation of δC^{13} and δO^{18} Within One Varve

Samples removed from the dark and light layers of nine separate varves illustrate a consistent enrichment of C^{12} and O^{16} in the dark material deposited in winter, and the relative enrichment of C^{13} and O^{18} in the lighter colored, summer layers (Table 5). Inasmuch as the carbonate deposited in the summer season was precipitated at higher temperatures than those of the winter season, it is obvious that temperature had little effect on the oxygen isotope ratios, because the observed distribution of O^{16} and O^{18} isotopes is directly opposed to that expected if temperature were the controlling factor. This situation may arise if the deeper portions of the lake in which all the varved sediments were preserved had been subject to only small temperature variations or if other factors influencing the δO^{18} values masked the temperature effect. Increased stream discharge during the summer would also tend to enrich the lake in O^{16}. The only important factor causing the enrichment of O^{18} in the carbonates appears to be evaporation, which, confirmed by the much greater quantities of calcium carbonate in the lighter layers, probably exerts the dominant control over the oxygen isotopic composition of the individual varves.

Isotopically light carbon dioxide, enriched in C^{12}, arising from the decay of organic matter in the sapropelic, dark-colored winter layer, appears to produce C^{12}-enriched carbonate during this season.

As a result of intense summer evaporation and pronounced decay of plant detritus under stagnant sapropelic conditions, the carbonate of the dark winter layers is characterized by relative C^{12} and O^{16} enrichment.

Correlation of Isotope Ratios with the Percentage of Calcium Carbonate of the Varves

The quantity of calcium carbonate in the 5- and 20-year samples was determined by Kirkland and Anderson using EDTA and DTA analysis (Appendix I). Linear regression and correlation statistics for δ C^{13} and the percentage of $CaCO_3$, and for δ O^{18} and percentage of $CaCO_3$ are presented in Table 6. Although the correlation coefficients, r, are not statistically significant at the 1 percent level, the slope of the regression line in each case is positive, suggesting that more positives values of δ C^{13} and δ O^{18} (C^{13} and O^{18} enrichment, respectively) are related to higher concentrations of calcium carbonate. This relationship is in accord with the observations made on the individual layers of single varves; that is, the lighter colored summer layers are characterized by high concentrations of $CaCO_3$ and relative enrichment of C^{13} and O^{18}. The correlation is poor, especially in the case of carbon, where the correlation coefficient is about half that of oxygen, and, although the relationship most likely exists, it is obscured by the operation of other factors.

Correlation of Carbon and Oxygen Isotope Ratios

The correlation coefficient (Table 6) computed using δ C^{13} and δ O^{18} as the variables for linear regression is highly significant at the 1 percent level, yielding a value of 0.67 for 107 samples. Since the slope of the regression line is positive, higher C^{13}/C^{12} ratios are associated with higher O^{18}/O^{16} ratios. This relationship is directly evident from Plate 6 and Figure 22, except for the first hundred years or so of the varved succession, in which they are inversely related. In samples comprising a number of varves, therefore, factors which tend to cause C^{12} enrichment also cause, or are associated with other factors which cause, O^{16} enrichment.

Correlation of Carbon and Oxygen Isotope Ratios with Time

The absence of any single trend in isotopic composition with time is readily observed by the cyclic? variation of δ O^{18} and δ C^{13} with time illustrated in Plate 6 and Figures 19–22.

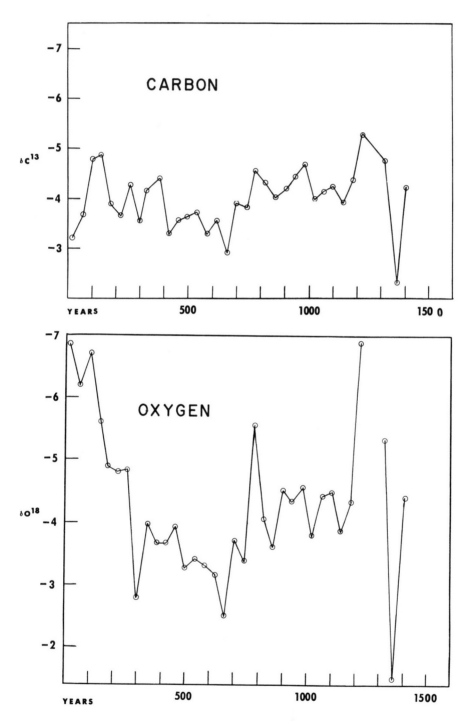

Figure 19. Variation of carbon and oxygen isotopic composition with time, using composite samples representing 40-year sedimentational intervals.

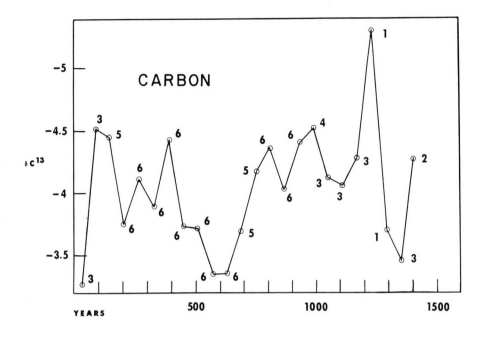

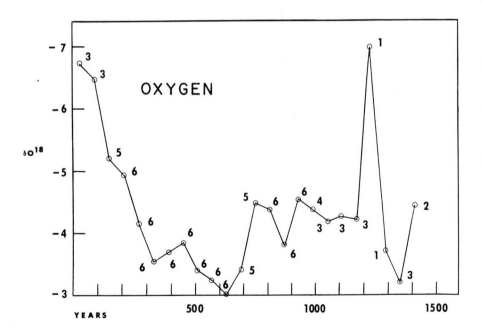

Figure 20. Variation of carbon and oxygen isotopic composition with time, using composite samples representing 60-year sedimentational intervals.

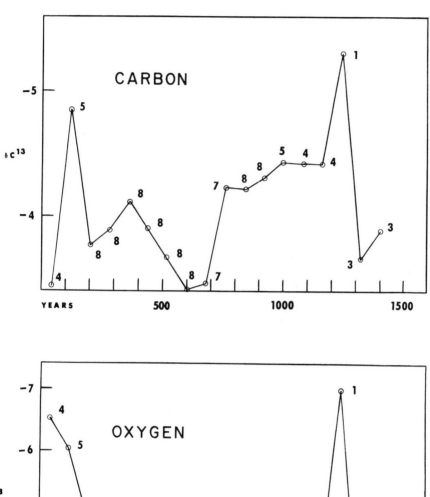

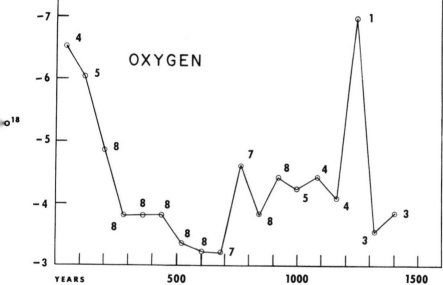

Figure 21. Variation of carbon and oxygen isotopic composition with time, using composite samples representing 80-year sedimentational intervals.

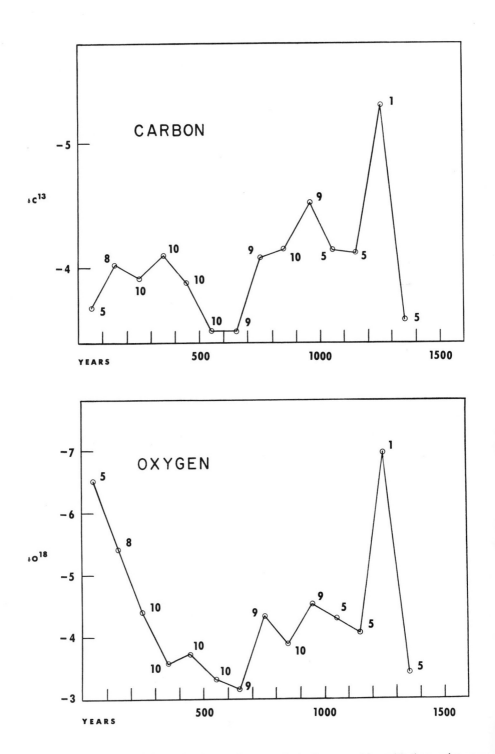

Figure 22. Variation of carbon and oxygen isotopic composition with time, using composite samples representing 100-year sedimentational intervals.

In order to illustrate better the long-term variations, samples analyzed individually were combined into composite samples representing periods of 40, 60, 80, and 100 years (Figs. 19 to 22). In most cases, the composite samples contain only half of the material deposited in the particular interval.

The most reliable representation of long-term trends in isotopic composition is perhaps Figure 22, in which the isotopic composition of each 100-year interval is plotted against time. The number of analyses incorporated in each point is shown on the graph and may be used as a rough guide to the significance of an individual value.

From the beginning of the varved sequence, arbitrarily assigned a value of zero years, $\delta\,C^{13}$ values (Fig. 22) appear to reach maxima at 0, 250, 600, and 1,050 years, resulting in periods between maximum C^{13} enrichment of 250, 350, and 450 years. Low (more negative) $\delta\,C^{13}$ values are recorded at 150, 350, and 950 years, creating periods between minimum $\delta\,C^{13}$ values of 200 and 600 years.

Low $\delta\,O^{18}$ values (Fig. 22) appear at 50?, 450, 750, and 950 years with intervening periods of 400?, 300, and 200 years. High $\delta\,O^{18}$ values are recorded at 350, 650, 850, and 1,150 years, with periods of 300, 200, and 300 years.

Except for the first few hundred years, the pattern exhibited by carbon isotope ratios is almost identical with the pattern of O^{18}/O^{16} ratios, high values of $\delta\,O^{18}$ generally appearing with high values of $\delta\,C^{13}$.

The most probable cause of "cyclic"? variation is climatic fluctuation; that is, alternation of dry intervals resulting in high evaporation rates, restricted plant cover, low stream discharge, and high temperatures, with relatively wet periods resulting in reduced evaporation, greater stream discharge, relatively luxuriant vegetation, and somewhat lower temperatures.

The isotopic responses to such climatic fluctuations as recorded by the carbonate sediments are as follows:

(1) Dry period

   (a) High evaporation rate — enrichment of O^{18}
   (b) Restricted vegetation cover adjacent to lake — depletion of C^{12} (relative enrichment of C^{13})
   (c) Low stream discharge — enrichment of O^{18}
   (d) High temperature — enrichment of O^{16}

(2) Wet period

   (a) Lower evaporation rates — enrichment of O^{16}
   (b) Increased stream discharge — enrichment of O^{16}
   (c) Increased vegetation cover — enrichment of C^{12}
   (d) Lower temperature — enrichment of O^{18}

If the temperature effect can be assumed to produce negligible changes in the O^{18}/O^{16} ratio of the carbonate deposited in the deeper portions of the lake,* periods of relative aridity would be recorded by carbonate sediments enriched in C^{13} and O^{18}, and intervals of increased rainfall would produce carbonates enriched in O^{16} and C^{12}. If this interpretation is correct, dry periods appear to have existed during the years when δC^{13} and δO^{18} values approached maxima in Figure 22.

The apparent anomaly, in which C^{12}/C^{13} ratios increase and O^{16}/O^{18} ratios decrease with time during the initial stage of varved deposition, thus far remains unexplained.

ACKNOWLEDGMENTS

Financial support from The National Science Foundation is gratefully acknowledged.

REFERENCES CITED

Craig, H., 1957, Isotope standards for carbon and oxygen and correction factors for mass spectrometric analysis of carbon dioxide: Geochim. et Cosmochim. Acta, v. 12, p. 133–149

Keith, M. L., and Weber, J. N., 1964, Carbon and oxygen isotopic composition of selected limestones and fossils: Geochim. et Cosmochim. Acta, v. 28, p. 1787–1816

Landergren, S., 1954, On the relative abundance of the stable carbon isotopes in marine sediments: Deep Sea Research, v. 1, p. 98–119

McKinney, C. R., McCrea, J. M., Epstein, S., Allen, H. A., and Urey, H. C., 1950, Improvements in mass spectrometers for the measurement of small differences in isotope abundance ratios: Rev. Sci. Instruments, v. 21, p. 724–730

Weber, J. N. and Keith, M. L., 1962, Isotopic composition and environmental classification of selected limestones and fossils (abs.): Geol. Soc. America Spec Paper 73, 259–260

Weber, J. N., Bergenback, R. E., Williams, E. G., and Keith, M. L., 1965, Reconstruction of depositional environments in the Pennsylvanian Vanport Basin by carbon isotope ratios: Jour. Sed. Petrology, v. 35, p. 36–48

---

*As suggested by the isotopic analyses of summer and winter layers of individual varves, where the summer layer was known to be deposited under conditions of higher temperature.

Statistical Analysis of the Rita Blanca
Varve Time-Series

Roger Y. Anderson

University of New Mexico, Albuquerque, New Mexico

L. H. Koopmans

University of New Mexico, Albuquerque, New Mexico

INTRODUCTION

Harmonic analysis and studies of component associations by means of the correlation coefficient have been used to help evaluate the changes in the Rita Blanca varve time-series. Harmonic analysis provides an objective estimate of periodic tendencies that variations in thickness, color, clay, and so on might exhibit. Correlation techniques were used to measure the association that various components have to each other. A third technique (cross-spectrum analysis), which is, in a sense, a combination of the first two, has been used to determine how the association of one component with another varies with frequency.

Six different kinds of measurements were obtained during the investigation of petrology (thickness, color, clay, calcium carbonate, tannin-lignin, and Kjeldahl nitrogen), and two (O^{16}/O^{18}, C^{12}/C^{13}) are available from the work of Weber (preceding chapter). All of these were investigated using the techniques mentioned above. The results are an adjunct to the discussion on petrology (Kirkland and Anderson, this report) and have been used in the interpretation of the environment (Part III, Synthesis).

The presence of laminations (in this case varves) makes it possible to develop a different approach to the study of harmonic variations in stratigraphic time series and this method has been applied to the Rita Blanca sequence. Data for all analyses were collected in alternate 5-year or composite 20-year units (Pl. 7) and converted to "absolute" (quantity per unit time) values using the methods outlined by Kirkland and Anderson in the paper in this report on petrology. Time-series for correlation, Fourier, power-spectrum, and cross-spectrum analysis of clay, calcium carbonate, Kjeldahl nitrogen, and tannin-lignin were constructed by grouping the analyses into units of 20 years (conversion to "absolute" values for thickness, color, and isotopes is not applicable). The result is a time-series of 51 units, each comprising 20 varves, for which comparisons can be made.

The conversion to "absolute" values permits the study of harmonic variations in independent time-series that are free from the distorting effects of percentage sampling (Anderson, 1967). It also permits bi-spectral analysis of independently measured components so that the degree and kind of associations may be determined at different frequencies.

HARMONIC ANALYSIS

The rhythmic or periodic nature of data collected in time-series has long been a subject of investigation. Early studies in a variety of areas were mainly subjective analyses of graphic data plots and produced inconclusive results (Anderson, 1961). More objective techniques of harmonic analysis have become available in recent years, and both Fourier and "power-spectrum" analyses have been applied to the study of varve time-series (Bryson and Dutton, 1961; Anderson and Koopmans, 1963). In addition to these measures of the variation of amplitude or "power" (mean-squared amplitude) with frequency, it has been found instructive to use a frequency-dependent measure of association for pairs of parameters for the varve series which behaves in virtually all respects like a correlation coefficient. The following discussion is intended to give the reader an intuitive introduction to this kind of analysis.

Two measured parameters on a varve time-series can themselves be thought of as numerical time-series $X(k)$ and $Y(k)$ where k denotes the year of observation, $k = 1, 2$, and so on; for example, $X(k)$ may represent the color index and $Y(k)$ the absolute clay content of the varve for the kth year of observation. Note that the time scale, although a relative one, is the same for both series. These time-series will be assumed to be purely random for this discussion, and ensemble averages will be denoted by E. Then, the assumption that the ensemble averages of the $X(k)$'s and $Y(k)$'s is zero will be written

$$EX(k) = EY(k) = 0, \; k = 1, \; 2, \text{ and so on.}$$

Now, under certain reasonable mathematical assumptions, the time series $X(k)$ and $Y(k)$ have Fourier decompositions

$$X(k) = \int_{-\frac{1}{2}}^{\frac{1}{2}} e^{2\pi i k f} \, dZ_x(f)$$

and

$$X(k) = \int_{-\frac{1}{2}}^{\frac{1}{2}} e^{2\pi i k f} \, dZ_y(f)$$

where, intuitively and imprecisely, $dZ_r(f)$ is a complex-valued random quantity which, when written in polar form,

$$dZ_r(f) = R_r(f) \quad \exp[i\theta_r(f)],$$

yields the amplitude $R_r(f)$ and phase angle $\theta_r(f)$ of the harmonic component of $X(k)$ at frequency f. A similar interpretation holds for $dZ_y(f)$. Now, to the association between $X(k)$ and $Y(k)$ at frequency f, it is only necessary to compute the complex analog of the correlation coefficient between the two complex-valued quantities $dZ_r(f)$ and $dZ_y(f)$:

$$R_{ry}(f) = \frac{E dZ_r(f) \overline{dZ_y(f)}}{\sqrt{E \mid dZ_r(f) \mid^2 E \mid dZ_y(f) \mid^2}}$$

where $\mid \quad \mid$ denotes absolute value and ‾ complex conjugate.

Compare this to the correlation coefficient for two real-valued random quantities X and Y:

$$r_{ry} = \frac{EXY - EXEY}{\sqrt{[EX^2 - (EX)^2] \, [EY^2 - (EY)^2]}}.$$

If $EX = EY = 0$, then the resemblance is more striking. The absence of the corresponding terms in the first equation is due to the fact that $E dZ_r(f) = E dZ_y(f) = 0$.

Now r_{ry} is a real-valued quantity with magnitude $\mid r_{ry} \mid$, which measures the strength of the association between X and Y and sign ($+$ or $-$) which measures the "direction" of this association. On the other hand, $R_{ry}(f)$ is a complex-valued quantity. Its magnitude $\mid R_{ry}(f) \mid$, called the coefficient of coherence, also measures the strength of an association, but it is now the association between the series $X(k)$ and $Y(k)$ at frequency f.

The phase angle $\theta_{ry}(f) = \arg R_{ry}(f)*$ indicates the "direction" of the association between $X(k)$ and $Y(k)$ in that it yields the (ensemble) average lead that the harmonic component of frequency f in the $X(k)$ series holds over the corresponding harmonic component in the $Y(k)$ series. Thus, if $\theta_{ry}(f) = 0$, at this frequency the series rise and fall in unison as a function of time. If $\theta_{ry}(f) = +180°$, the $X(k)$ series leads the $Y(k)$ series at f by $\frac{1}{2}$ cycle. In this case, as the component of the $X(k)$ series at frequency f rises, that of the $Y(k)$ series falls and conversely. If $\theta_{ry}(f) = -180°$, the same phenomenon is observed, except that now the $Y(k)$ series leads $X(k)$. In this

---

*If Z is a complex quantity, arg Z $=$ arctan (imaginary part of Z/real part of Z).

way, if $X(k)$ and $Y(k)$ both contribute to the thickness of the varve at time k, for example, if $X(k) + Y(k) =$ thickness of varve at time k — both the $X(k)$ and $Y(k)$ can have strong harmonics at frequency f; but if $\theta_{xy}(f) = \pm 180°$ and if the series are strongly coherent at f, the harmonics can cancel each other out, leaving little or no amplitude for the thickness series at this frequency. This phenomenon occurs in varying degrees for other values of $\theta_{xy}(f)$ in its range of values from $-180°$ and $+180°$.

In this report Fourier or amplitude analysis is used to study the frequency variations of the amplitude of a time-series to obtain high resolution in frequency (Fig. 23). The more gross variations of amplitude with frequency are studied by means of power spectra which are calculated in conjunction with the coherence and phase angles for pairs of time-series. For a more complete elementary discussion of the difference between power-spectrum analysis and Fourier analysis, the interested reader is referred to (Anderson and Koopmans, 1963). In that reference, the present impossibility of applying tests of significance to varve series is discussed in detail, and such statistical procedures are not used in the present report.

RESULTS OF ANALYSIS

Two components, clay and calcium carbonate, contribute to the thickness of each lamina. It has already been shown that the long-term variation of the two constituents is different (Fig. 17). The Fourier analysis of varve thickness change in the time-series (Fig. 23) measures the combined effect of both components, which probably reflect different processes operating in the basin. The Fourier spectrum of varve thickness has an increase in amplitude at about 22 years that rises above the general spectrum. It would be desirable to know if the clay and calcium carbonate differ in their contribution to the spectrum derived from thickness values alone — particularly in the region near 22 years where a possibly important period is indicated in the thickness spectrum. The two parameters were separated, and "absolute" values of calcium carbonate and clay were obtained in the manner described by Kirkland and Anderson earlier in this report. The separate analysis of each lamina was impracticable, but the effect of averaging 5-year $CaCO_3$ analyses will not alter the absolute clay and carbonate relationships at the frequencies of interest.

The Fourier spectrum of the clay time-series exhibits a slight increase in amplitude in the region between 10 and 12 years (Fig. 24). This increase is barely manifested in the total thickness spectrum. In contrast, the calcium carbonate spectrum (Fig. 25) has a prominent rise in amplitude at the 22-year period corresponding to the same peak in the thickness spectrum. Apparently the carbonate changes are principally responsible for the 22-year peak in the thickness spectrum. The climatic significance of variations in carbonate in some lake sediments is thought to have a positive relationship to temperature (Deevey, 1953, p. 298). One might conclude that a 22-year period was

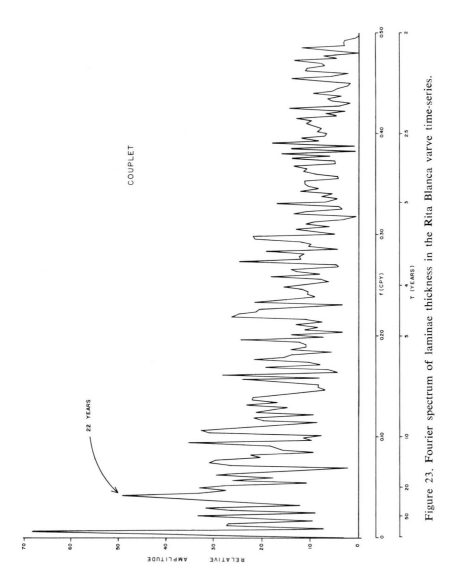

Figure 23. Fourier spectrum of laminae thickness in the Rita Blanca varve time-series.

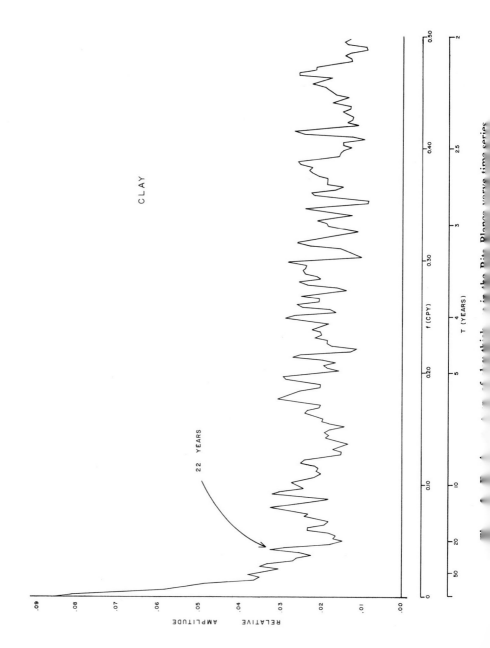

CLAY

RELATIVE   AMPLITUDE

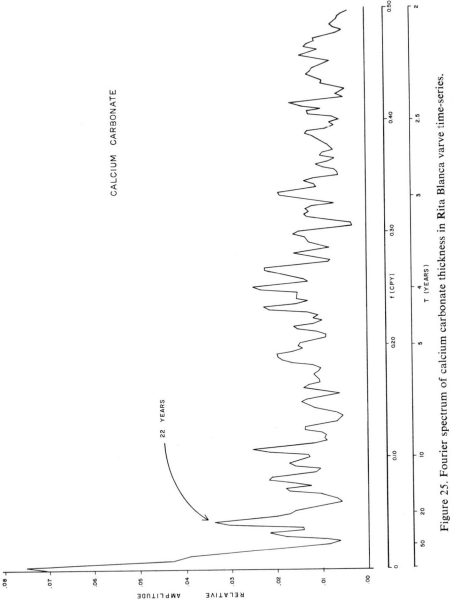

Figure 25. Fourier spectrum of calcium carbonate thickness in Rita Blanca varve time-series.

present in the temperature changes taking place at that time. Not all the factors are known, however, and one can say only that this is a reasonable conjecture. A 22-year period has appeared in the power spectrum analyses of several tree-ring series (Bryson and Dutton, 1961) and in some of the varve series analyzed by Anderson and Koopmans (1963). An obvious solar association is the 22-year Hale sunspot period which is manifested in the reverse polarity of sunspots and in the fundamental solar motion model reported in Jose (1965). The few examples noted so far are by no means proof that solar effects are reflected in temperature variations in the lower atmosphere, but they suggest that this line of investigation should be carried further.

The 1,400-year varve thickness series was also divided into 200-unit contiguous intervals, and each interval was analyzed separately. There was little similarity among the various 200-unit series, except that the majority had their highest peaks in the 100+-year region, and several exhibited the peak near 22 years observed in the 1,400-unit series (Fig. 26).

The thickness, carbonate, and clay spectra do not appear to show any other important tendencies toward periodicity. The high peaks in the neighborhood of 200 years reflect the long trends particularly obvious in the clay and carbonate records, but too few cycles are repeated to accurately assess the periodicity.

COMPONENT ASSOCIATION

The over-all dependence of all the parameters measured in the Rita Blanca series has been estimated by means of the correlation coefficient and power- and cross-spectrum analyses have also been used to clarify some of the associations.

Plate 7 illustrates graphically the synchroneity of the changes in the eight parameters measured. Table 7 shows the coefficients obtained from all possible correlations of the eight parameters. Two of these, thickness and color, are complex measures of processes operating in the basin, and the correlation coefficient gives an estimate of the role of the several factors contributing to each.

Both clay and calcium carbonate are contributors to thickness change (+0.68, +0.40), and the coefficients are in approximate accord with their proportion in the sediment. This does not mean that clay and calcium carbonate contribute to thickness in that proportion at the same time in the series. In fact, the opposite is the case, and each is alternately the component mainly responsible for thickness variation. If this were not the case, clay and calcium carbonate would correlate positively because they both have a positive relation to thickness. The clay–calcium carbonate correlation, however, is very low and negative (−0.12). However, a graph of the smoothed series of absolute clay and calcium carbonate clearly shows the inverse long-term association (Fig. 17).

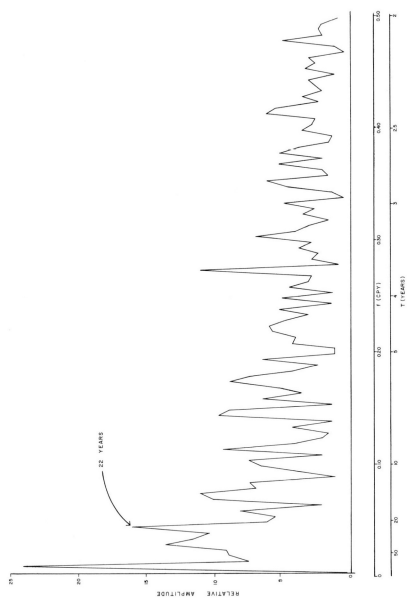

Figure 26. Fourier spectrum of the 200-unit thickness series for time interval $T_o + 701$ to $T_o + 900$.

TABLE 7. CORRELATION COEFFICIENTS FOR ALL POSSIBLE CORRELATIONS AMONG
THE EIGHT PARAMETERS MEASURED IN THE RITA BLANCA VARVE TIME-SERIES

Parameter examined	Thickness	Clay	CaCO$_3$	Tannin-lignin	Kjeldahl nitrogen	Color	O^{18}/O^{16}	C^{13}/C^{12}
Thickness	..	..	..	..	..	..	..	..
Clay	+0.68	..	..	..	..	..	..	..
CaCO$_3$	+0.40	−0.12	..	..	..	..	..	..
Tannin-lignin	+0.39	+0.64	−0.23	..	..	..	..	..
Kjeldahl nitrogen	+0.20	+0.85	−0.06	+0.45	..	..	..	..
Color	+0.15	+0.58	−0.58	+0.17	+0.52	..	..	..
O^{18}/O^{16}	−0.08	−0.12	+0.08	−0.17	−0.12	−0.15	..	..
C^{13}/C^{12}	−0.06	−0.05	+0.09	−0.08	−0.07	−0.07	+0.81	..

The graphs of the time-series (Pl. 7) show that color changes parallel those of almost all other parameters. Clay, calcium carbonate, and organic matter (Kjeldahl nitrogen) all have coefficients with color of about the same magnitude (+0.58, −0.58, +0.52). The close association of clay and organic matter (Kjeldahl nitrogen, +0.85) indicates that color change with time is mainly the result of the interplay of calcium carbonate and clay–organic matter. The determination of color index is a simple and rapid procedure, and, once the relation of color to other factors is known, the color index itself has value as a measure of changes taking place in the basin. Some very dark brown zones in the varve series yielded exceptionally high values for tannin-lignin, and the brown color was probably related to this component. However, other factors contributing to color apparently out-weigh the effect of tannin-lignin, which occurs in high concentration only in these few well-defined bands and has a correlation coefficient with color of only +0.17.

None of the isotopic correlations indicate an association to any of the other parameters, but there is a high positive correlation between the two isotopes (oxygen and carbon +0.81) in the series (*see* J. Weber, this report). All the coefficients, although too low to be important, are negative with the exception of the correlation with calcium carbonate. A positive correlation of O^{18}/O^{16} and calcium carbonate would be expected if high evaporation, which is chiefly responsible for the oxygen ratio, corresponded to increased calcium carbonate deposition.

POWER SPECTRA

Power spectra were computed for each parameter for consecutive 20-unit time intervals (Fig. 27). The power spectra for clay and calcium carbonate

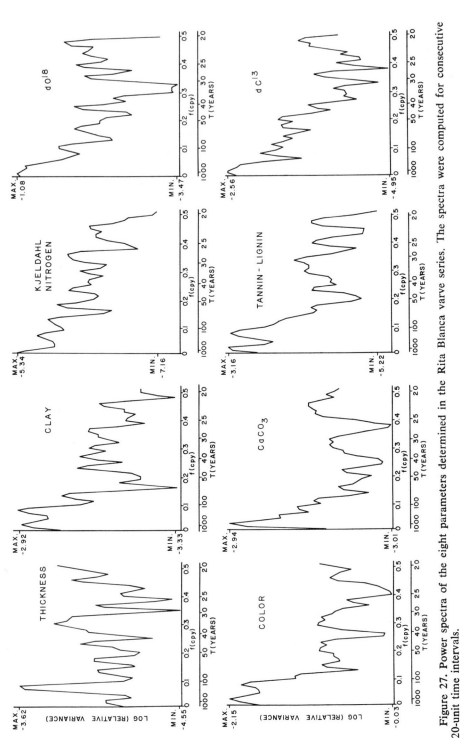

Figure 27. Power spectra of the eight parameters determined in the Rita Blanca varve series. The spectra were computed for consecutive 20-unit time intervals.

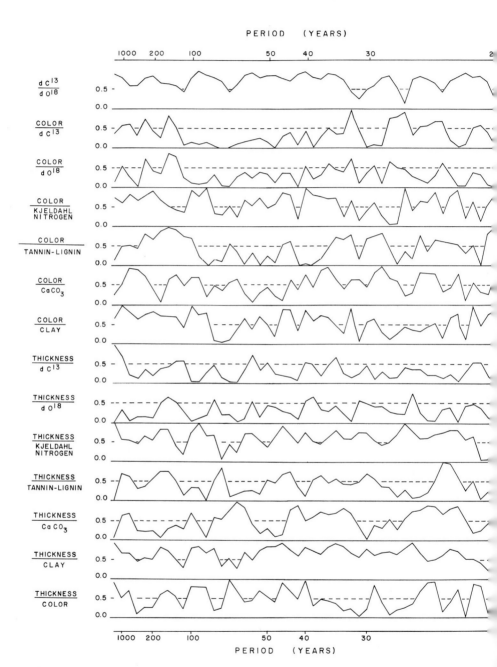

Figure 28. Coefficients of coherence of all combinations of the eight parameters determine in the Rita Blanca varve series.

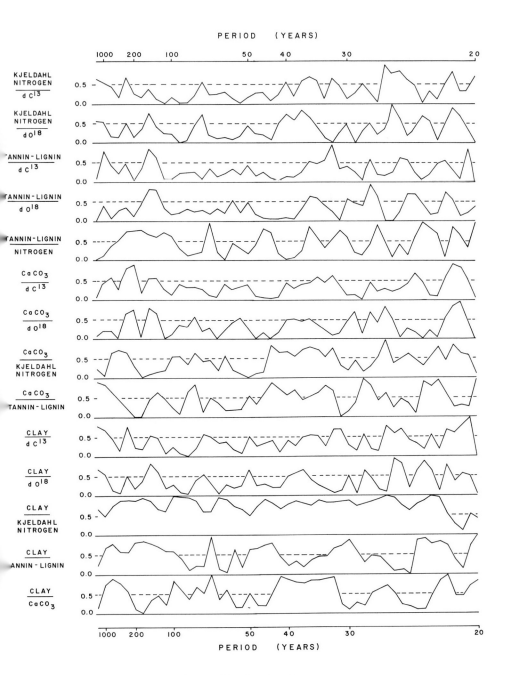

Figure 28. (Continued)

generally confirm the conclusions derived from the Fourier analyses discussed earlier. Both calcium carbonate and clay have spectra with the greatest power in the region above 150 years, but the carbonate spectrum has a prominent rise in power toward the shorter periods, with an additional peak at 22 years. The clay spectrum shows no increase toward the shorter periods. The tannic acid and nitrogen spectra most closely resemble that of clay and do not show the increase in power at the shorter periods. The spectra of the isotopes (O^{18}/O^{16} and C^{12}/C^{13}) resemble each other and the carbonate spectra, with an increase in power at the shorter periods. The power spectrum for color shows only a slight rise at the shorter periods and, like the thickness spectrum, appears to be an intermediate type. Although not directly related, the similarities and differences in spectra accord well with the interpretation of correlation coefficients: clay, nitrogen, and tannic acid being related; calcium carbonate being distinctly different and possibly related to the isotopes; and the composite measures (color and thickness) being intermediate types.

CROSS–SPECTRA

Cross-spectra were computed for all combinations of the eight parameters measured, and the coefficients of coherence are plotted in Figure 28. The graphs illustrate which frequencies are providing the greatest contribution to correlation. A general coefficient of coherence was computed for each parameter by averaging, frequency by frequency, all of the cross-spectra in which it occurred (Fig. 29a–h). An average of the coefficients of coherence was also computed for all 28 cross-spectra (Fig. 29i). The average of the 28 spectra shows the highest coherence in the region above 150 years and between 30 and 40 years. There is small average coherence between 40 and 100 years and only moderate average coherence for the shorter periods. Most of the summary spectra (Fig. 29a–h) show this same distribution of coherence to greater or lesser degree. Part of this consistency may be due to the use of thickness data in calculating the "absolute" values. However, three of the eight spectra (color, O^{18}/O^{16}, C^{12}/C^{13}) did not incorporate thickness data, and they also have the same distribution of coherence.

Clay and calcium carbonate are the most important measures of change in the varve series. All other parameters are dependent upon, or related to, these, with the possible exception of the isotopes. The clay–calcium carbonate cross-spectrum shows higher coherence at 22 years, 30–40 years, 80–90 years, and greater than 200 years. The 22- and 200+-year periods are also apparent in the cross and Fourier spectra previously discussed. The power spectrum for clay has a general rise between 30 and 40 years but does not resolve a peak between 80 and 90 years. The spectrum for calcium carbonate resolves a peak at 80–90 years that is largely masked by the higher adjacent peak, but it does not have an important increase in amplitude near 30–40 years.

The summary cross-spectrum for clay (Fig. 29) has the most uniform

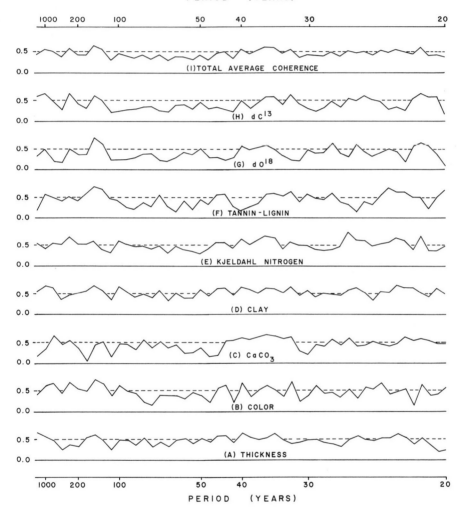

Figure 29. Average coherence values for each of the eight parameters in the Rita Blanca varve series (a–h) and the average coherence for all 28 cross-spectrum estimates (i).

coherence of all the parameters tested, whereas the calcium carbonate cross-spectrum (Fig. 29) has greater variation in coherence and is in close agreement with the individual cross-spectrum for clay–calcium carbonate (Fig. 28). This indicates that, of the two main components, carbonate is principally responsible for the variations of coherence.

PHASE RELATIONSHIPS

The analyses revealed a contradiction between the obvious strong negative association of clay and calcium carbonate that can be seen in Figure 17 and the low value for r (-0.12, Table 7). This prompted an examination of the phase angle relationships for the different frequencies. The phase angle is, for all practical purposes, an indicator of the positive or negative sign of the coherence. A theoretical discussion of the relationship between the correlation coefficient, coherence, and phase angle is given by Koopmans (1967).

A phase angle near 0° or 360° corresponds to a positive sign for the coherence at that frequency for the two parameters being tested. An angle near 180° corresponds to a negative sign for the coherence.

A comparison of frequency or period with phase angle for clay–calcium carbonate (Fig. 30) shows that negative correlations occur for periods longer than about 60–70 years, whereas the opposite is true for the shorter periods.

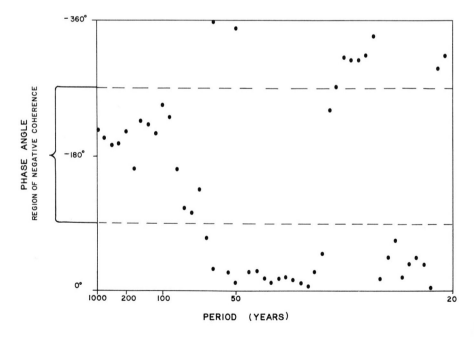

Figure 30. Phase angles for clay–calcium carbonate coherence coefficients. Note that longer periods have phase angles near 180°, indicating negative coherence or correlation.

This relationship helps explain the discrepancy between the obvious inverse variations in the smoothed curve of the two parameters and the low negative correlation obtained for clay–calcium carbonate. It is not known if the periods shorter than 20 years also have a positive clay–calcium carbonate association, but there is no reason to expect otherwise.

REFERENCES CITED

Anderson, R. Y., 1961, Solar-terrestrial climatic patterns in varved sediments: New York Acad. Sci. Annals, v. 95, p. 424–439

—— 1967, Sedimentary laminations in time-series study, *in* Merriam, D. F., *Editor,* Colloquium on Time-series Analysis: Kans. Geol. Survey Computer Contr. 18, p. 68–72

Anderson, R. Y., and Koopmans, L. H., 1963, Harmonic analysis of varve time series: Jour. Geophys. Res., v. 65, p. 877–893

Bryson, R. A., and Dutton, J. A., 1961, Some aspects of the variance spectra of tree rings and varves: New York Acad. Sci. Annals, v. 95, p. 580–604

Deevey, E. S., Jr., 1953, Paleolimnology and climate, *in* Shapely, Harlow, *Editor,* Climatic change, evidence, causes, and effects: Cambridge, Harvard Univ. Press, 318 p.

Jose, P. D., 1965, Sun's motion and sunspots: Astron. Jour., v. 70, p. 195–200

Koopmans, L. H., 1967, A comparison of coherence and correlation as measures of association for time and spatially indexed data, *in* Merriam, D. F., *Editor,* Colloquium on Time-series Analysis: Kans. Geol. Survey Computer Contr. 18, p. 1–4

Part III. Paleontology

Systematic List of Fossils in the Rita Blanca Lake Deposits

DOUGLAS W. KIRKLAND

Mobil Research and Development Corporation, Dallas, Texas

ROGER Y. ANDERSON

University of New Mexico, Albuquerque, New Mexico

The varved section of the Rita Blanca deposit contains many fossils, the most abundant of which are the alga, *Botryococcus;* pollen of *Artemisia,* Gramineae, and *Quercus;* leaves of *Quercus* and *Salix;* the ostracodes *Limnocythere* and *Cyprideis,* dragonfly nymphs of the family Libellulidae; midge pupae and adults of *Chironomus;* and the killifish *Fundulus.* In addition, there are a number of less common forms that add significantly to the environmental interpretation or the completeness of the reconstruction.

Classification of fossil insects is complicated by the overwhelming number of species; for example, there are some 250,000 species of modern beetles (Moore and others, 1952, p. 571). The curve of a wingvein, the presence of spines instead of hairs, or the morphology of mouth parts may be characteristics used to separate extant species. In the two-dimensional view of Rita Blanca insects, characteristics such as these often are missing or obscure.

Ostracodes present a taxonomic problem, inasmuch as Recent ostracodes are classified on the basis of their appendages. "Most ostracode neontologists do not regard variation in the features of the carapace as important in morphological studies" (Gutentag and Benson, 1962, p. 17). In order to classify Blancan ostracodes in a taxonomic system used for extant ostracodes, it is necessary to use a modified system based on carapace morphology.

The natural variation in the size and shape of leaves and the fact that many species, in particular, species of *Quercus* and *Salix,* hybridize freely

77

are the main problems involved in identification based on leaf morphology. Identification of species based on pollen and spore morphology involves consideration of many variables and has not been attempted.

Fossils were identified with extant species whenever possible. Classification of early Pleistocene fossils by a taxonomic system based on modern organisms is valid, but entails certain problems. New species may have developed during the Pleistocene in connection with climatic fluctuations and repeated displacements of the climatic zones, and the Blancan is far enough removed from the present that some speciation is probably involved for some of the forms.

The section on paleontology gives the systematics of most of the fossils found in the deposit to the level of extant identification possible. A few forms were recognized as being sufficiently different from modern forms to be considered as new species. The articles by paleontologists also relate observations concerning environmental associations and geographic distribution.

The following list of the Rita Blanca flora and fauna gives all the forms encountered in the study, plus their relative abundance as indicated by A, abundant; C, common; S, scarce; and R, rare. The list also includes a few forms not found by the investigators but referred to by earlier authors and some forms found by the investigators but not treated in one of the paleontologic articles.

Plant Kingdom

DIVISION CHRYSOPHYTA
  Class Xanthophyceae
    Order Heterosiphonales
      Family Xanthophyceae
        Botryococcus sp. (A)
  Class Chlorophyceae
    Order Chlorococcales
      Family Hydrodictyaceae
        Pediastrum sp. (S)
DIVISION BRYOPHYTA?
  Class Musci? (spores, A; plants, R.;
    Pl. 8, figs. 9, 10)
DIVISION PTERIDOPHYTA
  Class Lycopsida
    Order Lycopodiales
      Family Selaginellaceae
        Selaginella sp. (spores, R)
DIVISION SPERMATOPHYTA
Subdivision Gymnospermae
  Class Ephedropsida
    Order Ephedrales
      Family Ephedraceae
        Ephedra sp. (pollen, S)
  Class Conopsida
    Order Pinales

      Family Pinaceae
        Pinus sp. (pollen, S)
        Picea sp. (pollen, R)
        Abies sp. (pollen, R)
      Family Cupressaceae
        Juniperus sp. (pollen, S)
Subdivision Angiospermae
  Class Monocotyledoneae
    Order Pandanales
      Family Typhaceae
        Typha sp. (pollen, R)
      Family Sparganiaceae
        Sparganium? sp. (leaves, R)
      Family Najadaceae
        Ruppia maritima (leaves, fruits, C)
    Order Graminales
      Family Gramineae (pollen, A)
        Tribe Paniceae
        Panicum dichotomiflorum? (leaves, flower, R)
        Cenchrus pauciflorus (flower, R)
    Order Salicales
      Family Salicaceae
        Salix cf. *S. exigua* (leaves, A)

Salix bebbiana? (leaves, A)
Populus deltoides?
    (leaves, R)
Populus sp. (pollen, R)
Order Juglandales
  Family Juglandaceae
    Carya sp. (pollen, R)
    Juglans sp. (pollen, R)
Order Fagales
  Family Betulaceae
    Alnus sp. (pollen, R)
    Betula sp. (pollen, R)
    Corylus sp. (pollen, R)
  Family Fagaceae
    Quercus gambelii (leaves, C)
    Quercus stellata (leaves, C)
    Quercus ritablancensis
      n. sp. Tucker (leaves, C)
    Quercus sp. (pollen, A)
Order Urticales
  Family Ulmaceae
    Celtis sp. (pollen, R)
    Ulmus sp. (pollen, R)
  Family Moraceae
    Maclura pomifera (leaves, S)
  Family Urticaceae (pollen, R)
Order Polygonales
  Family Polygonaceae
    Eriogonum sp. (pollen, R)
Order Caryophyllales
  Family Chenopodiaceae or
  Amaranthaceae (pollen, S)
  Family Chenopodiaceae
    Sarcobatus (pollen, R)
    Tidestromia (pollen, R)
Order Rhoeadales
  Family Cruciferae (pollen, R)
    Brassica sp. (pollen, R)
Order Rosales
  Family Saxifragaceae
    Ribes sp. (leaves, R)
  Family Rosaceae (pollen, R)
    Crataegus chrysocarpa?
      (leaves, R)
    Prunus sp. (leaves, R)
  Family Leguminosae (pollen, R)
    Amorpha laevigata
      (leaves, R)
Order Geraniales
  Family Euphorbiaceae
    Croton sp. (pollen, R)
    Euphorbia sp. (pollen, R)

Order Sapindales
  Family Aceraceae
    Acer sp. (pollen, R)
  Family Sapindaceae
    Sapindus drummondii?
      (leaves, R)
Order Rhamnales
  Family Rhamnaceae
    Rhamnus? sp. (leaves, R)
Order Malvales
  Family Malvaceae (pollen, R)
Order Myrtiflorae
  Family Elaeagnaceae
    Elaeagnus sp. (pollen, R)
    Shepherdia sp. (pollen, R)
  Family Onagraceae (pollen, R)
Order Umbelliflorae
  Family Umbelliferae (pollen, R)
Order Ebenales
  Family Sapotaceae (pollen, R)
Order Contortae
  Family Oleaceae
    Fraxinus sp. (pollen, R)
Order Tubiflorae
  Family Polemoniaceae (pollen, R)
Order Asterales
  Family Compositae (pollen, C)
    Artemisia sp. (pollen, A)
    Baccharis salicina (leaves, R)

Animal Kingdom

PHYLUM MOLLUSCA
  Class Pelecypoda
    Order Teleodesmacea
      Family Sphaeriidae
        Pisidium? sp. (S)
        (Pl. 24, figs. 2, 4)
  Class Gastropoda
    Order Pulmonata
      Family Physidae
        Physa sp. (R)
PHYLUM ARTHROPODA
  Class Crustacea
    Subclass Ostracoda
      Order Podocopida
        Suborder Podocopina
          Superfamily Cypridacea
          Family Ilyocypridae
            Cyprideis sp. (A)
          Family Ilyocpyridae?
            Sp. (C) (Pl. 24,
            figs. 1, 3)

Family Candonidae
  Candona sp. (C)
Family Limnocytheridae
  Limnocythere sp. (A)
Class Insecta
  Order Odonata
    Suborder Anisoptera
      Family Aeshnidae
        Sp. (R)
      Family Libellulidae
        Sp. (A)
    Suborder Zygoptera
      Family Coenagrionidae?
        Sp. (R)
  Order Hemiptera
    Suborder Gymnocerata
      Superfamily Tingoidea
        Family Tingidae
          Sp. (R)
      Superfamily Lygaeoidea
        Family Lygaeidae
          Nysius? sp. (A)
    Hemiptera, position uncertain
      Sp. (R)
      Sp. (Lygaeidae,
        Corizidae, or
        Coreidae, R)
      Sp. (Lygaeidae,
        Pyrrhocoridae, or
        Corizidae, R)
      Sp. (Lygaeidae, cf.
        Ligyrocoris, R)
  Order Homoptera
    Suborder Auchenorrhyncha
      Family Cicadellidae
        cf. Deltocephalinae
          (R)
        Sp. (R)
        Sp. (R)
        Sp. (S)
      Superfamily Fulgoroidea-
      Areopodidae?
        Sp. (R)
  Order Coleoptera
    Suborder Adephaga
      Family Carabidae
        Sp., cf. *Selenophorus*
          (R)
    Suborder Polyphaga
      Superfamily Staphylinoidea
        Family Staphylinidae
          Sp., Aleocharinae?
          (R)

      Superfamily Cucujoidea
        Family Coccinellidae
          Hippodamia
            convergens? (R)
      Superfamily Melooidea
        Family Meloidae
          Lytta sp. (S)
          Epicauta sp. (R)
      Superfamily Scarabaeoidea
        Family Scarabaeidae
          Sp., cf. *Diplotaxis* (R)
      Superfamily Chyrsomeloidea
        Family Chyrsomelidae
          Sp., Chrysomelinae,
            cf. *Phaedon* (R)
          Disonycha sp.,
            Halticinae (R)
      Superfamily Curculionoidea
        Family Curculionidae
          Cleonus (Cleonidius)
            ritablancaensis
            Sleeper n. sp. (R)
          Cleonus (Cleonidius)
            channingensis
            Sleeper n. sp. (R)
  Order Trichoptera
    Family Mollanidae?
      Sp. (R)
  Order Diptera
    Suborder Nematocera
      Family Culicidae
        Culex sp. (R)
        Aedes sp. (R)
      Family Chironomidae
        Subfamily Chironominae
          Chironomus
            (Endochironomus)
            kirklandi Sublette
            n. sp. (A)
          Chironomus
            (Endochironomus)
            Sp. (R)
          ?Tanytarsus sp. (R)
        Subfamily Ortho-
        cladiinae?
          Sp. (C)
        Subfamily Tanypodinae?
          Sp. (R)
    Suborder Brachycera
      Family Bombyliidae
        Sp. (R)
    Suborder Cyclorrhapha
      Series Aschiza

Family Syrphidae
  Sp., cf *Syrphus* (R)
Series Schizophora
  Section Acalyptratae
    Subsection Acalyptratae
      Sp. (R)
  Section Calyptratae
    Sp. (R)
Order Hymenoptera
  Suborder Apocrita
    Superfamily Ichneumonoidea
      Family Ichneumonidae
        Sp. (R)
        Sp. (R)
        Sp. (Ichneumonoidea
          or Braconidae?, R)
    Superfamily Scolioidea
      Family Tiphiidae?
        Sp., cf. *Myzinum* (R)
      Family Formicidae
        Sp. (R)
        Subfamily Dorylinae-
          Ecitonini or
          Cheliomyrmicini
        Sp. (R)
        Subfamily Myrmicinae
        Sp. (R)
        Subfamily Formicinae
        Sp. (R)
    Superfamily Vespoidea
      Family Pompilidae
        Sp. (R)
    Superfamily Apoidea
      Sp. (R)
      Sp. (R)
Order Hymenoptera, position
  uncertain
    Sp. (R)
    Sp. (R)

    Sp. (R)
Insecta, position uncertain
  Sp. (leafhopper?, R)
  Sp. (Hemiptera?, R)
  Sp. (Hymenoptera?,
    R)
  Sp. (cf. Tipulidae?, R)
  Sp. (Homoptera-
    Aphididae?, R)
  Sp. (Diptera,
    Hymenoptera,
    Coleoptera, R)
PHYLUM CHORDATA
  Class Osteichthyes
    Order Antheriniformes
      Family Cyprinodontidae
        Fundulus cf.
          F. zebrinus (A)
    Order Perciformes
      Family Centrarchidae
        Lepomus cf.
          L. megalotis (S)
  Class Mammalia
    Order Perissodactyla
      Suborder Hippomorpha
        Superfamily Equoidea
        Family Equidae
          Nannippus phlegon
          Equus (Plesippus)
            simplicidens
    Order Artiodactyla
      Family Camelidae
        Gigantocamelus
          spatulus
    Order Proboscidae
      Suborder Elephantoidea
        Family Gomphoteriidae
          Stegomastodon sp.

REFERENCES CITED

Gutentag, E. D., and Benson, R. H., 1962, Neogene (Plio-Pleistocene fresh-water ostracods from the central High Plains: Kans. Univ. Geol. Survey Bull. 157, pt. 4, 60 p.

Moore, R. C., Lalicker, C. G., and Fischer, A. G., 1952, Invertebrate fossils: New York, McGraw-Hill, 766 p.

Pollen Profile of the Rita Blanca Lake Deposits[1]

JERRY HARBOUR

U.S. Geological Survey, Flagstaff, Arizona

COLLECTION AND PROCESSING

Samples for pollen analysis of the Rita Blanca deposits were collected by the author December 28, 1958, from a section 4.7 m (15.4 feet) thick at the outcrop designated Locality A (Fig. 3). Continuous series of channel samples were taken at 10 cm intervals through the lower 3.2 m and at 15 cm intervals through the upper 1.5 m of the section. (The deposits are all early Pleistocene [Blancan] in age [*see* Part I, Introduction].) The samples were processed by Bernard C. Arms, Geochronology Laboratories, University of Arizona, using a flotation cell and HF-KOH treatment. Counting was done at the same Laboratories with the direction and assistance of Dr. Jane Gray.

Approximately 13,000 pollen grains were counted from 24 stratigraphic intervals and one modern sample from a cattle tank. The total number of grains counted in each sample (Σ P) is shown on the pollen profile (Fig. 31) and includes only pollen, except in sample 7, which includes one *Selaginella* spore.

RESULTS

Pollen occurs abundantly and continuously in the section between the 60 cm level and the 350 cm level (Fig. 31). The varved portion of the section at this locality occurs between the 137 cm level and the 263 cm level, with approximately 80 cm of polliniferous section above and below the varved sediments.

The pollen profile is dominated throughout by *Artemisia*, which averages about 45 percent of the total pollen, and by approximately equal amounts of

---

[1]Publication authorized by the Director, U.S. Geological Survey.

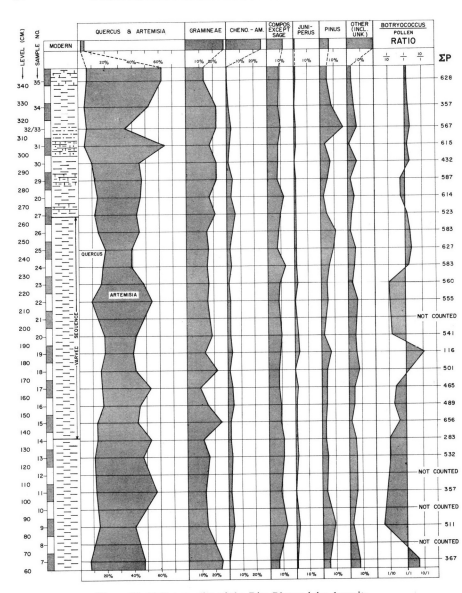

Figure 31. Pollen profile of the Rita Blanca lake deposits.

Quercus and Gramineae pollen, which together comprise about 30 percent of the total. The remainder of the pollen consists of Compositae other than sage, *Pinus* (possibly derived from long-distance transport), Chenopodiaceae or Amaranthaceae, *Juniperus,* and 30 types which account for less than 2 percent of the total.

Variations in the profile result largely from changes in the percentage of the predominant sage pollen, but no significant trends are obvious. An unusual aspect of these deposits is the great abundance of the alga *Botryococcus* (Pl. 9, fig. 3), whose cells were several times as abundant as pollen grains in many of the samples (Fig. 31). Another aquatic alga, *Pediastrum,* which is commonly encountered in samples from lacustrine deposits, was seen only rarely in a few levels from the Rita Blanca section.

MODERN POLLEN, VEGETATION, AND SOILS

The modern pollen assemblage is quite different from the Rita Blanca fossil assemblages. The modern assemblage, taken from a nearby cattle tank, is dominated by Gramineae, Chenopodiaceae or Amaranthaceae, and Compositae pollen other than sagebrush. It is possible that the large number of chenopods, and perhaps composites, growing on disturbed ground immediately adjacent to the cattle tank, may have caused their pollen to be over-represented in the modern sample. *Artemisia* and *Quercus* pollen combined account for only 7 percent of the modern assemblage. The modern pollen types and their percentages are:

28%	Gramineae (possibly under-represents local flora)	2%	*Quercus*
26%	Chenopodiaceae or Amaranthaceae	2%	*Croton* cf. *C. texensis*
12%	Compositae other than sagebrush	1%	Umbelliferae
7%	*Pinus* (not growing in area today)	1%	?Urticaceae
5%	*Artemisia* (probably *A. filifolia,* the most abundant species in the area today)	+	*Picea* (not growing in area today)
		+	*Euphorbia*
		+	?Portulacaceae
3%	Malvaceae	+	*Mimosa*
		10%	Unknown

The present vegetation in the area is a mixed-grass prairie association. Tall and short grasses, chenopods, and composites predominate on the treeless plains. Cottonwood trees (*Populus deltoides*) abound in Mathews Draw at the site, and are probably the most abundant valley tree in the region today. Mesquite (*Prosopis juliflora*) is common on the breaks of the plains and on many valley slopes. Other trees and shrubs seen in the larger nearby valleys include *Quercus, Juniperus, Juglans, Prunus virginiana, Celtis,* and *Ulmus.* C. M. Rowell, Jr. (1958, A provisional checklist of the flora of the Texas Panhandle based on collections made in the summers of 1955 and 1957; mimeographed for private circulation, 11 p.) has reported "*Acer saccharum* Marsh vel aff." [sic] as a known importation established in the Canadian River Valley, which lies about 10 miles south of the Rita Blanca basin.

The present soils in the area are chiefly deep calcareous sandy silt and silty sand. Extensive areas of sand hills occur in some of the larger valley bottoms and in some localities on the plains. Clayey soils are essentially confined to the numerous small local basins of Pleistocene age which dot the plains surface. Modification of the plains surface since deposition of the underlying (Pliocene) Ogallala Group has been principally by downcutting of a few widely spaced streams and by reworking of surficial Ogallala material. Surface drainage is very poorly integrated in the region. Therefore, the soil materials in the area today are representative, at least in a general way, of materials available during the early Pleistocene.

FOSSIL POLLEN TYPES

Artemisia
(Pl. 9, figs. 1, 2)

The grains of *Artemisia* from the Rita Blanca deposits show little variation in size, structure, and surface ornamentation, making the direct identification of subtypes, if any, impossible. However, the marked predominance of *Artemisia* over all other pollen types (Fig. 31) probably indicates that it was frequent or dominant in the fossil flora of the region. Today, extensive nearly pure stands of the genus in the United States are essentially restricted to shrub species which occur from the Rocky Mountains to the Great Basin. As the most abundant species of *Artemisia* found in this northern desert shrub climax is *A. tridentata* (big sage), it is suggested that it may be the principal species represented in the Rita Blanca deposits. According to Kearney and Peebles (1960, p. 941) *A. tridentata* is indicative of a deep, fertile, nonsaline soil, a close approximation of the soils in the area today. The easternmost natural occurrence of the species has been reported as small isolated stands on the edge of the Texas High Plains within 50 miles west of the Rita Blanca basin.

Quercus
(Pl. 8, figs. 3, 4)

The pollen grains of *Quercus* in the Rita Blanca deposits show considerable variation in surface ornamentation and wall thickness, but less pronounced variation in size. This may suggest that several kinds of oak are represented in the deposits, a conclusion which is supported by the leaf fossils. An inverse relationship between the numbers of *Quercus* and *Artemisia* pollen can be seen in more than half the changes in their pollen curves (Fig. 31), which may suggest that the two genera were in close competition and that the oaks, therefore, were shrubs rather than trees. This possibility is supported in the leaf flora by the predominance of small leaves and by the fact that two of the identified types (*Quercus stellata* and *Q. gambelii*) usually are shrubby forms.

Gramineae
(Pl. 8, fig. 8)

No attempt was made to identify the types of grasses in the pollen flora. However, the fossil pollen flora contained far fewer large grass grains than the modern cattle tank samples. (The relatively large grains in the modern sample may be due to natural floristic differences, but possibly they reflect the local presence of cultivated forms in the modern assemblage.)

Compositae other than sagebrush
(Pl. 8, fig. 7)

Three pollen-morphological types of composites were identified in this category: low-spined Tubuliflorae, high-spined Tubuliflorae, and Liguliflorae. The last type was very rare. Owing to the tremendous number of species involved and the wide range of environments that they encompass, all were grouped and plotted as a single element on the pollen profile.

Pinus
(Pl. 8, fig. 1)

In all the fossil samples except one (no. 32/33) the pine pollen amounted to less than 10 percent of the total pollen, with an average of about 6 percent. This is very similar to the modern cattle-tank sample which contained 7 percent. Since the modern pine pollen must have come from areas 50 to 100 miles to the west, it seems likely that the fossil pine pollen may have had a similar distant origin. Sample 32/33, with 17 percent pine pollen, probably does not indicate the presence of pine in the Rita Blanca area during the brief period represented.

Other modern examples of long-distance transport of pine pollen in the region are illustrated by the occurrence of 9 to 15 percent pine in three other cattle-tank samples from localities along the Texas–New Mexico border (Hafsten, 1961, Fig. 32–33). In the same study, a pine forest of Wisconsin age on the Texas High Plains almost certainly is indicated by many samples in which pine pollen comprises 50 to 98 percent of the total pollen present.

Juniperus
(Pl. 8, fig. 2)

Juniper pollen occurs in small quantities (up to 3 percent) in almost every fossil sample. The delicate nature and the difficulty of recognizing even large fragments of this pollen grain may have resulted in a slight underrepresentation of the fossil population. Juniper occurs today in sheltered gorges along the margins of the High Plains, but is more typical of the pinyon-juniper woodlands occurring at elevations of 4,500 feet to about 7,000 feet in the western interior states.

Chenopodiaceae or Amaranthaceae
(Pl. 8, fig. 5)

Three pollen-morphological groups were recognized among the families Chenopodiaceae and Amaranthaceae: *Sarcobatus* and *Tidestromia,* both of which were very rare, and undifferentiated Chenopodiaceae and Amaranthaceae which ranged narrowly between 1 and 6 percent of the pollen present in all of the polliniferous samples. A great contrast between the modern and the fossil assemblages is seen in this group, since the undifferentiated Chenopodiaceae and Amaranthaceae pollen comprises 26 percent of the pollen in the modern sample.

OTHER POLLEN TYPES

The remaining fossil-pollen elements consist of 30 types which altogether comprise only 1.6 percent of the total grains counted. These may be divided into 8 types which are trees, 4 types which may be either trees or shrubs, 7 types which are shrubs, and 11 herbaceous types:

Trees	Trees or shrubs	Shrubs	Herbs
Abies	*Alnus*	*Corylus*	*Brassica*
Acer	*Celtis*	*Elaeagnus*	*Croton*
Betula	*Fraxinus*	*Ephedra*	Cruciferae
Carya	Leguminoseae	Malvaceae	*Eriogonum*
Juglans		Rosaceae	*Euphorbia*
Picea		Sapotaceae	Onagraceae
Populus		*Shepherdia*	Polemoniaceae
Ulmus			*Selaginella* (spore)
			Typha
			Umbelliferae
			Urticaceae

Unknown types and severely damaged grains comprise about 4 percent (range 2 to 7 percent) of the total fossil-pollen assemblages.

Eleven fossil types belong to genera that do not occur in the area today. They are: *Abies, Alnus, Betula, Carya, Corylus, Elaeagnus, Fraxinus, Pinus, Picea, Selaginella,* and *Shepherdia. Acer,* as previously mentioned, is introduced in the region, but established in favorable locations. Of the foregoing genera, *Pinus, Picea,* and *Abies* pollen grains probably are present in the Rita Blanca sediments because of long-distance transport by the wind. Pollen grains from the other genera may have been similarly introduced or they may have come from riparian forms which grew near the shore of the Pleistocene lake. The abundant forms of pollen that occur in the deposits are illustrated in Plates 8 and 9.

ENVIRONMENTAL INTERPRETATION

The degree of representation of the actual fossil flora by the pollen and leaf fossils is influenced by two factors. First, the pollen mainly represents those elements of the original population which were wind pollinated. Second, the leaf flora probably over-represents the riparian forms in the original population — that is, those which grew along the banks of the lake and its contributory streams. Therefore, environmental interpretations based on the leaf flora alone probably would indicate a more moist climate than the fossil pollen flora. This view is supported by the statistical distribution of moist climate and dry climate forms in the pollen profile. If pine is discounted as an element in the original local population, sage, oak, and grasses comprise about 85 percent of the total grains counted in the profile, and the forms which do not grow in the area today (*see* above) account for only 1 percent of the pollen in the fossil samples. Furthermore, the most abundant pollen element, *Artemisia,* is not reported in the megafossil assemblage.

The larger number of individual fossils and the larger number of plant types represented in the fossil pollen flora probably indicate that it is more representative of the over-all original population than is the leaf flora. Therefore, an interpretation of the climate prevailing during the part of Blancan time represented by these deposits primarily depends upon the selection of an area with a modern floristic assemblage closely resembling the nonriparian fossil pollen assemblage. The sagebrush, oak, and grass pollen assemblage is analogous to the plant associations of the sagebrush belt or the chaparral belt of the Rocky Mountains, or of the sagebrush association of the northern desert shrub community of the Great Basin and Colorado Plateau. However, oak is not as important an element in the last association as in the first two. According to Shantz and Zon (1924, p. 8), there is a general altitudinal succession in places in the Rocky Mountains from sagebrush (*Artemisia* spp.) at lower elevations, to chaparral (*Quercus gambelii, Cercocarpus parvifolius,* and *Amelanchier*), and to pinyon-juniper woodlands at higher elevations. In their discussion of the pinyon-juniper woodlands the same authors (Shantz and Zon, 1924) state that pinyon and juniper alternate over thousands of square miles with sagebrush, "the former occupying rough broken country or shallow stony soil, while sagebrush occurs on the more level ground, which has a deep, uniform soil." The flat topography and deep, well-drained soils postulated for the Rita Blanca area are through most, if not all, of the Pleistocene would have provided the physical setting for the sagebrush component of such an alternation, if similar climatic conditions existed. Therefore, it seems likely that the fossil pollen flora could have been produced under climatic conditions analogous to those found somewhere today between the higher parts of the northern desert shrub community and the lower parts of the pinyon-juniper woodlands in the Rocky Mountains.

Pure stands of sagebrush in the northern desert shrub climax are characterized today by a dry climate having rainfall more or less evenly distributed throughout the year, with a total precipitation of only 10 to 15 inches per year (Shantz and Zon, 1924, p. 21). The climate of the alternating pinyon-juniper woodlands and sagebrush "flats" is slightly moister than that of the northern desert shrub community, but precipitation seldom exceeds 20 inches per year. In both vegetation areas the climate averages about 5° colder than that of the Rita Blanca area today, and the frost-free period averages only about 90 to 120 days compared to about 150 to 180 days for the Rita Blanca area at present (Visher, 1954). Potential evaporation is comparable in all the mentioned areas and exceeds the precipitation by a considerable margin. However, potential evaporation decreases somewhat with increasing altitude because of the general relationship between evaporation and temperature. Figure 32 diagrams the relationship between altitudinal zonation and climatic conditions in the areas discussed.

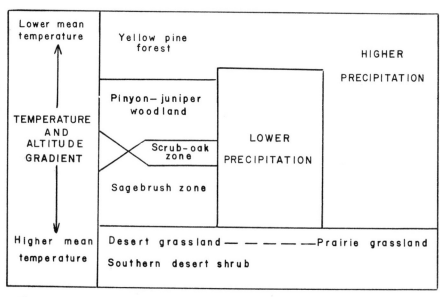

Figure 32. Relationship of altitudinal floral associations to climatic conditions along a zone of equal latitude.

In Figure 32, the present vegetation of the Rita Blanca area would fall in the Prairie Grassland category, and the fossil flora, based on the dominant pollen association (sagebrush-oak-grass) is believed to fall somewhere in the vicinity of the midpoint of the column depicting altitudinal succession. This would suggest that the climate during the deposition of the Rita Blanca lacustrine deposits was both colder and drier than the modern climate of the area.

By using the conditions of precipitation, temperature, and evaporation that now prevail in the analogous vegetation areas, it is estimated that precipitation during this part of the Blancan averaged about 15 to 20 inches per year, and both the summer and winter mean temperatures probably were about 3° to 5°F colder than at the present. Potential evaporation probably was lower than at present, perhaps in the range of 45 to 55 inches per year.

If the Blancan floral assemblage and climatic conditions are correctly interpreted from the pollen profile, then the Rita Blanca area during this time may be described as a sagebrush plain with stands of scrub oak and scattered junipers either mixed with the sagebrush or growing on well-drained valley slopes. Valley bottoms and the lakeshore probably were lined with broad-leaved deciduous trees, and had an undercover of small shrubs and herbs. Grasses also probably grew on the sagebrush plain.

RELATIONSHIP BETWEEN CHANGES IN POLLEN PROFILE AND VARVE COMPOSITION

The relationship between the partial pollen profile and the rate of carbonate deposition through the varved portion of the section exposed at Locality A is shown in Figure 33. The predominant pollen elements, *Artemisia, Quercus,* and Gramineae are plotted on the partial profile from a coincident zero percentage line. The scale of the carbonate deposition curve is plotted in the opposite direction of the pollen percentage scale to permit a direct comparison of the inverse behavior of the carbonate and *Artemisia* curves. To simplify plotting of the carbonate deposition curve, its vertical scale is proportional to the arithmetic thickness of the varves at this locality (9.01 cm per 100 varves). Since the varve and pollen studies were made at different times by different investigators, the vertical stratigraphic positions of the lowermost and uppermost varves within pollen samples 14 and 27, respectively (Fig. 31), are known only to within about ±2 cm. However, inspection of Figure 33 will show that this possible disagreement between the two plots is too small to affect significantly the relationships between their curves.

The abundance of *Botryococcus* cells, relative to pollen grains, is shown in a parallel plot on Figure 33 as the *Botryococcus*/pollen ratio. To obtain this ratio, individual cells were counted regardless of clustering seen on the microscope slides. This counting technique was used because it was thought

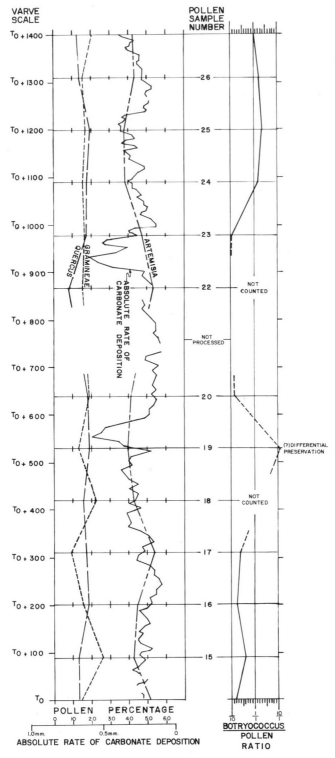

Figure 33. Relationship between sediment composition and the partial pollen profile in the varved part of the Rita Blanca lake beds (Locality A).

to be more representative of the abundance of the alga, since there was no knowledge nor control of the breakage of colonies during processing of the samples. The average number of cells observed in clusters on the microscope slides is estimated to be 3 per cluster. Many single cells were seen, and clusters of as many as 12 to 15 cells were quite rare.

A weak inverse correlation between the percentage of *Artemisia* pollen and the rate of carbonate deposition is evident in the graphs in Figure 33. Since carbonate deposition probably was directly related to mean summer temperature, the abundance of *Artemisia* pollen may be inversely related to summer temperature. Through most of the varved section, changes in the percentage of *Artemisia* seem to be mirrored by inverse changes in *Quercus* percentages. The proportion of Gramineae pollen in the samples remains almost constant at about 15 percent.

The *Botryococcus*-to-pollen ratio curve shows an approximate direct relationship to the carbonate-deposition curve. Such a relationship would imply that the abundance of *Botryococcus* increased during periods of higher mean summer temperatures. Continuous varve deposition is believed to be *prima facie* evidence for continuously abundant, perennial water in the Blancan lake; therefore, availability of water may be discounted as an important influence on alga production. The complete, or nearly complete, absence of any chlorides or sulfates in the Rita Blanca varved sediments indicates that these ions were not available in the source rocks of the drainage basin; therefore, changes in salinity may be discounted as an influence on *Botryococcus* production. The highly calcareous nature of the sediments is good evidence that evaporation exerted an important influence on lake sedimentation.

Differential preservation of *Botryococcus* has clearly affected its relative abundance in three levels below the varved sediments, and possibly in one level within the varved sequence (Fig. 31, pollen sample 19). Samples 4, 5, and 6, taken below the polliniferous part of the section, yielded almost no pollen, but each showed several hundred *Botryococcus* cells. The abundance of *Botryococcus* in these samples probably indicates its greater resistance to weathering than the pollen found in the sediments. Similarily, pollen sample 19, which was taken within the varved sequence (Fig. 31), was quite poor in pollen, with only 116 grains on two complete slides, and it had the highest *Botryococcus*-to-pollen ratio of all samples within the polliniferous part of the section at this locality.

SUMMARY AND CONCLUSIONS

Abundant, well-preserved pollen occurs continuously throughout a thickness of 2.9 m (9.5 ft) of calcareous lacustrine clay in the early Pleistocene Rita Blanca deposits. The polliniferous section includes the varved sediments which are the main subject of investigation in this volume. The pollen profile of the entire polliniferous section is dominated by *Artemisia,* and the pollen assemblage principally consists of *Artemisia, Quercus,* and Gramineae, with some Compositae other than sagebrush, and undifferentiated Chenopodiaceae–Amaranthaceae. *Juniperus* is present in very minor amounts (3 percent or less) in almost all of the fossil pollen spectra. All of these pollen-morphological types are represented by species which grow in this prairie grassland area today. However, the distribution of fossil pollen types differs from both the distribution of pollen types in the modern sample and the distribution of plant types in the modern landscape. *Pinus, Picea,* and *Abies* pollen are winged types and are regarded as grains introduced by wind-transport in the modern and fossil pollen assemblages. Only about 1 percent of the remaining fossil pollen types were recognized as coming from genera that do not grow in the region today, and some of these grains may have been introduced by the wind, also. Most of the genera represented by these minor pollen types require a relatively moist environment today, and if they were actually present in the local Blancan landscape they probably were riparian, or lake-border, elements.

The *Artemisia-Quercus*-Gramineae fossil pollen association is analogous to the modern plant associations occurring between the lower part of the pinyon-juniper woodlands and the uppert part of the sagebrush zone of the northern desert shrubs in parts of the Rocky Mountains, Colorado Plateau, and Great Basin. If the analogy between the fossil pollen association and the modern plant association is correct, then the climate of the Rita Blanca area during this part of the Blancan stage should be closely comparable to the climate of the modern analogous vegetation areas. On this basis, the reconstructed climate is interpreted as having averaged 3° to 5°F colder annually than at present, and as having 1 to 5 inches less annual precipitation. Annual potential evaporation probably was somewhat less than the modern rate, perhaps in the range of 45 to 55 inches per year, and the average annual frost-free period may have been 30 to 60 days shorter than at present.

The climatic conditions interpreted from the pollen evidence can not be categorized clearly as either "pluvial" or "interpluvial." The generally low temperature and short frost-free period may imply that the time was one of glacial advance farther north. If this is true, it does not support the concept of synchrony between glacial advance and pluvial conditions in nonglaciated regions. However, the climate of the time might have been strongly influenced by the proximity of continental glaciation which, during the early Pleistocene, extended into northeastern Kansas, about 500 miles away.

The pollen evidence certainly does not indicate a subtropical climate, which has been proposed for most of the Blancan by Hibbard (1960) mainly on the excellent basis of the widespread occurrence of large fossil reptiles in some of the Blancan sediments of this region. Allowing that the large reptiles are valid indicators of subtropical climate for parts of the Blancan, then the sagebrush-dominated pollen profile from the Rita Blanca basin is clear evidence that other periods of Blancan time were cold and dry. Another example of Blancan climatic changes is suggested by two isolated pollen assemblages reported by Gray (1960, p. 146–147) from the Safford Basin in southeastern Arizona. One assemblage resembles the modern plant assemblage there, which is typical of the Lower Sonoran Life Zone, but the other pollen assemblage suggests the presence of a pine forest, with some fir, and possibly spruce, growing in the area.

Comparison of changes in the pollen profile with changes of sediment composition within the varved sequence provides a means of cross-checking environmental interpretations. The approximate inverse correlation between the *Artemisia* pollen curve and the carbonate deposition curve implies that the relative abundance of *Artemisia* was related to cooler summers, because the rate of carbonate deposition probably was directly related to mean summer temperature.

Throughout the varved sequence the *Botryococcus* cell-to-pollen grain ratio shows an approximate direct relationship to the carbonate deposition curve and an approximate inverse relationship to the *Artemisia* pollen curve. These relationships imply that *Botryococcus* production may have been directly or indirectly related to changes in summer temperatures. When the entire polliniferous section is considered, however, no consistent relationship between the *Botryococcus* curve and any of the pollen curves is obvious. Inspection of the upper and especially the lower, parts of the profile (Fig. 31) reveals a general similarity in the behavior of the *Botryococcus* curve and the Gramineae curve in these parts. This similarity would seem to be in general agreement with the implied *Botryococcus*-temperature relationship.

The outstanding feature of the pollen profile, including the varved section, is its uniformity. No really significant changes in pollen ratios seem to have occurred, in spite of considerable variation in the composition of the lake sediments. Apparently much longer term climatic trends, or stronger climatic flunctuations than those inferred for the Rita Blanca lake area, would have been needed to bring about gross changes in pollen ratios.

REFERENCES CITED

Gray, Jane, 1960, Micropaleobotanical research on the late Tertiary sediments of Arizona: Ariz. Geol. Soc. Digest, v. 3, p. 145–149

Hafsten, Ulf, 1961, Pleistocene development of vegetation and climate in the southern High Plains as evidenced by pollen analysis, *in* Wendorf, D. F., Paleoecology of the Llano Estacado: Santa Fe, N. Mex. Mus. Press, p. 59–97

Hibbard, C. W., 1960, An interpretation of Pliocene and Pleistocene climates in North America, The President's Address: Mich. Acad. Sci., Arts and Letters 62d Ann. Rept., p. 5–30

Kearney, T. H., and Peebles, R. H., 1960, Arizona flora, 2d ed.: Berkeley and Los Angeles, Calif. Press, 1085 p.

Shantz, H. L., and Zon, Raphael, 1924, The natural vegetation of the United States, *in* Baker, O. E., 1936, Atlas of American Agriculture: Washington, U.S. Govt. Printing Office, 29 p.

Visher, S. S., 1954, Climatic atlas of the United States: Cambridge, Harvard Univ. Press, 403 p.

Oak Leaves of the Rita Blanca Lake Deposits

JOHN M. TUCKER

University of California, Davis, California

INTRODUCTION

Oak leaves are the most abundant specimens in the Rita Blanca fossil leaf flora. Fifty-nine fossil specimens were collected. These include Gambel's oak (*Quercus gambelii*), post oak (*Quercus stellata*), and a number of specimens that cannot be referred to an extant form and are described here as a new species (*Quercus ritablancensis*). The excellent state of preservation of a number of these fossil leaves (note, especially, Pl. 9, fig. 4) suggests that they grew in the immediate vicinity of the lake. From this, and from their relative abundance in the fossil flora, it may be inferred that the oaks formed a dominant element in the lakeside vegetation.

The descriptive section contains a few comments on the present distribution of related forms which is followed by a brief environmental interpretation.

SYSTEMATIC DESCRIPTIONS

Class ANGIOSPERMAE
Order FAGALES
Family FAGACEAE
Quercus gambelii Nutt.
(Pl. 9, figs. 4, 5)

A number of fossil leaves resembles this species to a greater or lesser degree. They seem to fall within the range of variation of the species as a whole, but are somewhat atypical for the most part — in addition to being quite small, they have slightly too few lobes and petioles that are a little too short in proportion to the leaf as a whole.

Quercus gambelii is a deciduous oak primarily of the Rockies and the higher mountains of the Southwest, occurring most commonly in the ponderosa pine zone. A number of isolated outlying populations — doubtless relictual from some period of moister climate

— occurs in sheltered sites on mesas and canyons considerably to the east of the foot-slopes of the Rockies. The nearest locality to the Rita Blanca area known to the writer is on the headwaters of Tramperos Creek in Union County, New Mexico, approximately 75 miles west-northwest of the fossil area.

COLLECTION: Figured specimens, 44, 33; referred specimen, 27.

Quercus ritablancensis n. sp.
(Pl. 9, fig. 8; Pl. 10, fig. 1)

DESCRIPTION: Leaves 4.0–5.5 cm in length, 2.4–3.2 cm in width; shallowly lobed, with one or two nonpaired lobes and one or two additional obtuse teeth on each side, the lobes truncate or obtusely pointed; base broadly cuneate to rounded; apex obtuse; petiole moderately stout, 3–6 mm in length; midrib fairly strong; four to six irregular secondaries on each side of midrib, diverging at angles of 50° to 60°, craspedodrome, those entering the major lobes bifurcated; occasional irregularly spaced intersecondaries; tertiary venation reticulate; texture coriaceous.

DISCUSSION: This group of small, shallowly lobed leaves is not readily referable to any Recent North American oak. On the one hand, they are not sharply separable from certain of the fossils here referred to *Q. gambelii,* although, in general, they fall con-siderably outside the normal range of variation of that species. On the other hand, the smallest of these fossils bears a slight resemblance to the modern *Q. pungens* Liebm. Any relationship with the latter species, however, would not be close. *Quercus pungens,* a xerophytic shrub of dry, rocky slopes in the mountains of the Southwest, is not adapted to severe winters, and even today extends no farther north than the Guadalupe Moun-tains of extreme southern New Mexico.

Quercus ritablancensis is visualized as a small-leaved, relatively xerophytic, and prob-ably shrubby oak. Its rather sparse representation in the fossil flora, in comparison with the preceding and the following species, suggests that it may have occupied drier sites at some distance from the lake.

COLLECTION: Holotype, 373, paratype, 58; referred specimens, 410, 430.

Quercus stellata Wangenheim
(Pl. 9, figs. 6, 7)

The wide-ranging post oak of the eastern and middle-western states reaches its present western limits in west-central Oklahoma and Texas. The two fossils in Plate 9 can be matched quite well by a collection of this species from near Durham, Roger Mills County, Oklahoma (*Tucker, 3274A*). The present-day existence of hybrids of *Q. stellata* (with *Q. havardii* Rydb.) in a number of localities in the Texas panhandle indicates that the post oak ranged farther to the west at some time in the past, doubtless under more mesic conditions (*see* Muller, 1952). The fossils may be matched also by speci-mens of *Q. margaretta* Ashe, a species of the Gulf Coast closely related, and often very similar in leaf form, to *Q. stellata.* The fossils are best identified as the latter species, however, on the basis of present-day distributions and the extant hybrids of *Q. stellata* in the Texas panhandle.

Several other fossil leaves (308, 407, 449) — all fragmentary — are classified as this species with considerable reservation, inasmuch as they are also suggestive of *Q. lyrata* Walt., the overcup oak of the lower Mississippi Valley and the Southeast. They are much smaller than is typical for *Q. lyrata,* however, and it is not inconceivable that they repre-sent merely aberrant leaves of *Q. stellata,* considering the multiplicity of leaf forms of that widespread and variable species. *Quercus lyrata,* furthermore, is a tree of swamps and river-bottom forests, and seemingly would have been far less likely than *Q. stellata* to have produced a xerophytic offshoot capable of persisting in the Rita Blanca area during Blancan time. Considering their fragmentary character, therefore, plus the other factors presented above, to regard these fossils as a typical *Q. stellata,* rather than *Q. lyrata,* would seem to be the more reasonable interpretation.

COLLECTION: Figured specimens, 13, 20; referred specimens, 281, 337.

CLIMATIC INFERENCES

The problem of drawing climatic inferences from these fossil oak leaves alone is fraught with difficulties. Inasmuch as the Upper Pliocene was a period of deflation in the southern High Plains, the mere presence of a moderately deep permanent lake in the Rita Blanca basin during Nebraskan time (where none is maintained under the present climate) would indicate that moister conditions than prevail today must have existed at least during the period when the lake developed. Whether or not this was still the case during the period when the varved clays were laid down may be open to question. By the same token, the mere presence of *Q. gambelii* and *Q. stellata* in the Rita Blanca deposits may not provide a sound basis for conclusions regarding climatic conditions, but, in order for these species to have migrated into the area in the first place, the climate must have been moister for a time than it is today. Once established in the area, however, it is quite conceivable that these species could have persisted along lake borders for some time even though the subsequent overall climatic trend was one of increasing drought. Neither of these oaks occurs in the region at present, and it seems highly probable that insufficient moisture is the principal factor barring their occupancy of the area.

The high percentage of *Artemisia* pollen in the pollen flora at all levels in the Rita Blanca deposits, coupled with the low levels of pine pollen, must be considered a strong indication of relatively dry conditions. The small size of the oak leaves, moreover, would suggest xerophytic forms of their species. Considered in this context, the oak leaves (most of which doubtless represent an element of the lake border vegetation) probably have less significance than the pollen flora as an indicator of the over-all regional climate. In this connection, it is well to bear in mind MacGinitie's observation (1953, p. 45–46) that fossil floras composed largely of riparian types can often appear deceptively mesophytic.

REFERENCES CITED

MacGinitie, H. D., 1953, Fossil plants of the Florissant beds, Colorado: Carnegie Inst. Washington Pub. 599.

Muller, C. H., 1952, Ecological control of hybridization in *Quercus*: A factor in the mechanism of evolution: Evolution, v. 6, p. 147–161

Fossil Flora of the Rita Blanca Lake Deposits

WILLIAM C. MARTIN

University of New Mexico, Albuquerque, New Mexico

INTRODUCTION

This paper deals with that part of the fossil flora of the Rita Blanca deposits (excluding the oaks, which are presented by J. M. Tucker in the preceding paper) as represented by leaf, stem, and fruit compressions, the majority of which are in the form of leaf impressions.

Although many of the fossil specimens are in remarkably good condition, others are very fragmentary, and characteristics are obscured; thus, some material is essentially unidentifiable even to family level. But in other instances of questionable identification, certain fragments are tentatively referred to particular families.

Taxonomically speaking, the Rita Blanca material is in a somewhat awkward position, that is, not old enough for sweeping changes to have occurred in the taxonomic relationships of species entities, but old enough for minor changes to have been possible. Therefore, due to the unavailability of sufficient clues required for description of new taxa, the material is compared with extant forms, and present-day nomenclature is followed in all instances.

SYSTEMATIC DESCRIPTIONS

Class MONOCOTYLEDONEAE
Order PANDANALES
Family SPARGANIACEAE
Sparganium? sp.
(Pl. 10, fig. 2)

One triangular fragment of leaf tip displaying distinct parallel venation compares with leaf tips on certain herbarium specimens of *Sparganium* (bur reed). Some question exists, however, as to the true identity of this specimen, since similar leaf characteristics exist in other aquatic families such as Alismaceae and Najadaceae. No additional vegetative parts or any fruiting material was evident.

101

As species of this genus occur widely in marshy places or in streams throughout North America, the Rita Blanca representatives probably grew in comparable habitats in the lake or in streams flowing into the lake. There is no indication, however, that this plant was an important member of the Rita Blanca flora.

COLLECTION: 325.

Family NAJADACEAE
Ruppia maritima L.
(Pl. 10, fig. 3)

Probably the most interesting plant in this fossil collection was identified as *Ruppia maritima,* or ditch grass. This plant was tentatively identified as a moss, but further examination indicated a close resemblance to ditch grass in the elongate, filiform leaf fragment, in the size and shape of the fruits, and in the clustered, possibly branched nature of the pedicels.

A part of the inflorescence and a short section of a filiform leaf are all that remain of the plant. Two clusters of fruit were preserved, both arranged on elongated, filiform pedicels. The fruit which averages 1.1 mm in width and 2.0 mm in length is generally ovate. The leaf fragment is filiform, 0.8 mm wide at the widest point and 25 mm long; the apex long-acute. Other filiform leaf fragments somewhat remote from the inflorescence may well be *Ruppia* also, but the connection cannot be made with any degree of certainty.

This fossil closely resembles *Ruppia maritima,* an aquatic plant which is practically cosmopolitan in modern floras but usually inhabits saline waters. The presence of this plant in the Rita Blanca flora is interesting in that this species may be one of the clues to the composition of Rita Blanca Lake if the present habitat preferences of *Ruppia* are any indication of the nature of its Pleistocene habitat.

COLLECTION: 309.

Order GRAMINALES
Family GRAMINEAE
Panicum dichotomiflorum? Michx.
(Pl. 10, fig. 4)

Several specimens belonging to the grass family are recognized in this study, but in most cases only fragments are available.

In two examples, in which only a part of the inflorescences are apparent, the material showed a resemblance to that of *Panicum dichotomiflorum* (panic grass). No fruiting material was evident, but examination of the branches of the inflorescence indicated a rather close resemblance to that of *Panicum.*

The largest inflorescence is about 8.5 cm long and, of course, is only a part of the entire unit. The widely spreading branches are slender to nearly capillary, and each bears a characteristic swelling at the base. No leaves, flowers, or fruits could be definitely identified or associated with this material.

Panicum dichotomiflorum can be expected nearly anywhere in moist ground or waste places over much of the United States and, if present during the Pleistocene in the Rita Blanca area, was probably fairly common in moist areas near the lake.

COLLECTION: 85, 136.

Cenchrus pauciflorus Benth.
(Pl. 10, fig. 5)

The identification of this specimen is also based on a portion of an inflorescence, in this instance a single spikelet and a short section of the pedicel. No leaves or other parts were seen.

Cenchrus pauciflorus (sandbur) is applied to this specimen, since the spikelet or bur is without a ring of bristles at the base and falls generally within the spikelet size range characteristic of this species. The sandbur is wide ranging in the Western Hemisphere and shows a preference for open, often sandy areas. This species may have grown in open ground along the borders of the lake, but probably did not comprise a part of the composition of the wooded areas along the streams or lake shore.

COLLECTION: 275.

Class DICOTYLEDONEAE
Order SALICALES
Family SALICACEAE
Salix

Numerous specimens of willow are represented in the collection, these comprising nearly 25 percent of the specimens studied. Identification of these willows is very difficult and is based entirely on leaf comparisons, since fruiting material is not evident.

Salix cf. *S. exigua* Nutt.
(Pl. 10, figs. 6, 7, 8; Pl. 11, fig. 1)

Several leaves and leaf fragments bear a resemblance to this species in general size and shape. All of the leaves appear to be entire margined, a condition exhibited only in some of the modern coyote willows, but falling easily within the normal range of variation of this species.

Salix exigua is common throughout many of the southwestern states, ranging into northern Mexico and normally inhabiting areas along streams from grasslands of the plains regions to middle altitudes in the mountains. Judging from the high frequency of fossils of this type, this species must have been a common form of the Rita Blanca streamside and lakeside vegetation.

COLLECTION: 273, 425, 451, B-31.

Salix bebbiana? Sarg.
(Pl. 11, fig. 2)

Fragments of leaves of a broad-leaved, entire-margined form of willow fit this category. Bebb willow is an occasional shrub or small tree of riparian situations ranging from Canada and Alaska south into California, New Mexico, and eastward into the northeastern states. It was probably not a common entity in the composition of the Rita Blanca area.

The majority of the remaining willow leaves appears not to be related closely to either of the above species. Although the leaf margins are entire as noted in the previously described species, the leaf apices (when present) appear to be acuminate and often falcate. This pattern seems to fit only *S. caroliniana* Michx. in our modern flora. Sometimes called the coastal plain willow, this large shrub is now found primarily in the Southcentral states, ranging west to Texas and Kansas along streams and other bodies of water.

Whatever the nature of this taxon, it apparently was an important part of the Rita Blanca riparian flora, as evidenced by the presence of several representatives in the fossil collection.

COLLECTION: B-9.

Populus deltoides? Marsh
(Pl. 11, figs. 3, 4)

This species is represented by four leaf fragments. Although only parts of leaves are available, the large crenate-dentate marginal teeth and venation patterns leave little doubt as to the generic relationships. The truncate leaf bases, when present, gave some basis for calling these specimens either *P. deltoides* or *P. sargentii;* however, examination of the petiole indicate this structure to be free of glands, a characteristic of *P. deltoides* (populus eastern cottonwood).

The cottonwoods were probably an abundant component of the streamside vegetation and possibly also were common along the shores of the lake. The present distribution of these trees covers most of eastern and midwestern United States and must have been widely distributed during the Pleistocene.

COLLECTION: 45, 278.

Order URTICALES
Family MORACEAE
Maclura pomifera (Raf.) Schneid.
(Pl. 11, fig. 5)

Three specimens of broadly lanceolate, acuminate, entire leaves resemble osage-orange in shape and size (16 mm wide by 35 mm long) and in the short petiole.

This taxon is widely distributed throughout the midwest, extending south into Texas, and was an occasional tree in the Rita Blanca flora.

COLLECTION: 289.

Order ROSALES
Family SAXIFRAGACEAE
Ribes sp.

Two leaf fragments are comparable to leaves of this genus in size, with an average of 22.5 mm in width, and appear to be three to five lobed. Also, the major veins are arranged in a palmate fashion.

Ribes probably grew along breaks or slopes of low rocky hills or sparsely wooded areas in the vicinity of the lake.

Insufficient material is represented to arrive at species designations in these specimens.

COLLECTION: 243, 470.

Family ROSACEAE
Crataegus chrysocarpa? Ashe
(Pl. 11, fig. 6)

One leaf fragment exhibits characteristics similar to those of leaves in the genus *Crataegus*. The hawthorns are an extremely difficult group taxonomically, and a fragment of a single leaf is little help in establishing species relationships. Enough of this leaf is available to indicate a lobed condition and a doubly serrate margin. The petiole is intact and appears to be slightly winged.

The most likely species to have occurred in the Rita Blanca area is *C. chrysocarpa* Ashe, a small tree commonly found from the Rocky Mountains through the eastern part of the United States and into Canada. It generally exists in rough or rocky areas along streams. Thus, it may well have been a part of the riparian flora near Rita Blanca Lake during the Pleistocene, but could have been expected nearly anywhere in the area.

COLLECTION: 185.

Prunus sp.

This genus is represented by a single, small, elliptical leaf which is finely glandular serrate on the margin.

COLLECTION: B-32.

Family LEGUMINOSAE
Amorpha laevigata (Nutt.) Torr. and Gray
(Pl. 11, figs. 7, 9)

Three leaflets strongly suggest a close relationship to *Amorpha laevigata* in the obovate shape, rounded to slightly emarginate apices, entire margins, and short-cuneate bases. In addition, there appears to be a suggestion of a glandular punctate condition of the leaflet blades, as well as glands at the top of the petiolule in one specimen.

Smooth indigo-bush is a papilionaceous shrub with odd-pinnate, pellucid-punctate, compound leaves. It now inhabits riparian habitats in the South-Central States from Oklahoma and eastern Texas to Arkansas and Louisiana.

It is conceivable that this plant was a part of the riparian flora of the Rita Blanca times, possibly growing near the shores or the lake.

COLLECTION: 130, 436.

Order SAPINDALES
Family SAPINDACEAE
Sapindus drummondii? Hook. and Arn.
(Pl. 11, fig. 10)

Two fossil specimens resemble the leaflets of *Sapindus* in the lanceolate shape, long acuminate and falcate tips, entire margins, and rounded-acute bases. There is also some indication that these leaflets were slightly undulate.

The short petiolule (about 3 mm long) is attached to what appears to be a bit of the rachis of the compound leaf. The leaflets are essentially complete and average 11 mm in width and 43 mm in length.

Sapindus drummondii (western soapberry), a small tree with compound leaves, is found in moist situations along streams throughout the southern and southwestern states. This tree was probably an occasional riparian form in the study area.

COLLECTION: J.E. 361.

Order RHAMNALES
Family RHAMNACEAE
Rhamnus? sp.

This identification is made with some hesitation, as only leaf fragments are available. These fragments indicate the leaves were probably ovate-obtuse and entire on the margins and had a venation pattern similar to that of *Rhamnus*.

COLLECTION: 277, 280.

Order ASTERALES
Family COMPOSITAE

The Composites must have been very numerous in the Rita Blanca flora but apparently were not as common under riparian situations, as evidenced by the dearth of fossil specimens which can be referred to this family.

Baccharis salicina Torr. and Gray
(Pl. 11, fig. 8)

Two specimens in particular seem to belong to this genus. One of them, a leaf, appears to fit *B. salicina* in size, 4 mm wide and 17.5 mm long, the lanceolate shape, the entire-to-remotely toothed margin, the subsessile base, and the 3-nerved pattern of venation.

The second example closely fits the characteristics of the fruit of *Baccharis* also in the size of the achene, less than 1 mm in length, the longitudinally ridged pericarp, and the capillary pappus.

B. salicina is a much branched shrub up to 6 feet in height and is presently found in *Artemisia* and Pinyon areas from Texas and Kansas to Colorado and New Mexico. In the Rita Blanca flora this species probably inhabited open, moist areas such as clearings near streams.

COLLECTION: 256, 267.

ENVIRONMENTAL INFERENCES

It is apparent that woody plants are more numerous than herbaceous species in the Rita Blanca fossil record, owing probably to the woody plants having more resistant vegetative parts and the likelihood that these plants tended to drop their leaves into the streams and lake in great numbers, an opportunity not as available to herbaceous plants.

In any case, the majority of the specimens appears to represent a riparian type of vegetation, but this should not be considered to be an indicator of the flora of the Rita Blanca area. The material only indicates the existence of an extensive riparian situation in the vicinity of the lake and along streams flowing into the lake.

This study gives no definite indication of the nature of the climate of this region, although it was probably considerably drier than these specimens would indicate.

The significance of *Ruppia* in the flora should not be overlooked. The present-day existence of this plant in waters with greater than normal salinity or alkalinity suggests a similar association in Rita Blanca Lake.

SELECTED REFERENCES

Harrington, H. D., 1954, Manual of the plants of Colorado: Denver, Sage Books, 666 p.

Hitchcock, A. S., 1950, Manual of the grasses of the United States, 2d ed. (revised by Agnes Chase): U.S. Dept. Agriculture Misc. Pub. 200.

MacGinitie, H. D., 1953, Fossil plants of the Florissant beds, Colorado: Carnegie Inst. Washington Pub. 599.

Rydberg, P. A., 1932, Flora of the prairies and plains of central North America: New York, New York Bot. Gardens, 969 p.

Tidestrom, I., and Kittell, Sister, 1941, A flora of Arizona and New Mexico: Washington, D.C., Catholic Univ. America Press, 750 p.

Vines, R. A., 1960, Trees, shrubs and woody vines of the Southwest: Austin, Univ. Tex. Press, 1104 p.

Ostracodes of the Rita Blanca Lake Deposits

RICHARD H. BENSON

Smithsonian Institution, Washington, D.C.

INTRODUCTION

The fossil carapaces of three genera of ostracodes are found in great abundance in the varved Rita Blanca lake beds. Although poorly preserved and difficult to extract individually, ostracode specimens compose an important part of the light-colored, calcareous-rich layers. Their restricted distribution within the varves and the unusual assemblage of taxa they represent may shed some light on the possible environments of deposition of these lacustrine strata.

The purpose of this report is to describe the kinds and significance of the ostracodes found, to suggest some possible identifications of species, and to compare the occurrence of these fossils with analogous occurrences of similar living forms. Because taxonomically diagnostic characters could be examined in only a relatively few well-preserved specimens, much information remains obscure until better material can be found. Knowledge of late Cenozoic fresh-water ostracodes in North America is sparse. Even actual living species are in the early stages of description. The conclusions are therefore more limited than might be possible in the future when more comparative data are available.

The slabs of rock containing varves and the specimens that are discussed here were collected by Roger Y. Anderson and Douglas W. Kirkland. The author is indebted to them for this material and for the background data from their study.

TAXONOMIC DISCUSSION

Three genera of ostracodes are represented among the specimens examined. *Limnocythere,* which is usually rare in fresh-water ostracode assemblages, is extremely abundant in the light-colored varve layers and is present in some darker colored layers. *Candona,* a very common fresh-water form, was found

107

only in a few of the many dark-colored layers examined. *Cyprideis,* a common brackish-water ostracode genus, was abundantly represented in some of the lighter colored layers.

A fourth ostracode genus, *Ilyocypris,* originally was thought to be present after a preliminary study of mashed, partly preserved specimens, but that these forms are in fact ostracodes is uncertain. Attempts to find specimens with muscle scars, identifiable marginal areas, or other diagnostic features proved unfruitful.

The identification and classification of living fresh-water species largely depends upon knowledge of the appendages and other "soft-part" anatomy, together with that of rather detailed carapace morphology. Identification of poorly preserved fossil specimens at the species level, based solely on the exterior configuration of the carapace, is not practical at this stage of knowledge of most fresh-water ostracodes. The following discussion is therefore directed at description of those carapace features that were seen, and that serve to support the generic and species group identifications.

Limnocythere sp.
(Pl. 21, figs. 1, 2, 6, 7, 8; Pl. 22, figs. 1, 2, 3)

Hundreds of valves per square inch of one or more species of *Limnocythere* were found in the light-colored layers of the varved sediment. Specimens of this genus are usually the only ones represented in a given light-colored layer. Even where *Cyprideis,* the other genus occasionally found with *Limnocythere,* occurred, *Limnocythere* constituted more than 90 percent of the specimens present.

The characteristics that helped to identify *Limnocythere* (Pl. 22, figs. 1, 2, 3) were the elongate-to-subrectangular lateral profile of the carapace with evenly subrounded but unequal ends, the two dorsolateral sulci, a smooth-to-reticulate surface, an adductor muscle-scar pattern composed of a vertical row of four scars with an antennal scar fairly distant toward the anterior (seen in a few specimens), and a moderately wide marginal strip or duplicature found in the adults. It is interesting that, even though few muscle-scar patterns could be studied, divided median adductor scars, as illustrated by Sars (1925, Pl. 69, fig. 2) were observed. The vast majority of specimens observed were immature molts. Males and females were found, but usually in poor condition, as the carapaces of the adults were very thin and frequently distorted. The male is generally larger (Pl. 22, fig. 3) and more elongate than the female (Pl. 22, fig. 2).

Limnocythere is superficially like *Ilyocypris* in that the fragile carapaces of both genera are subrectangular and have dorsolateral sulci in the areas of the adductor and antennal muscle-scars. Also, both are subreticulate, possibly tuberculate, to smooth or pitted. However, they are actually members of separate superfamilies. *Limnocythere* belongs to the Cytheracea, a predominantly marine taxon, and *Ilyocypris* to the Cypridacea, a predominantly fresh-water taxon. Although the general shapes of these two forms are distinct to the experienced eye, they can be easily confused, especially if diagenetic compression of the sediments has distorted this shape. The most reliable differences are recognizable in the muscle-scar patterns and, to some extent, the marginal areas or configuration of the duplicature and radial-pore canals. In *Limnocythere* the adductor muscle-scar pattern consists of an isolated vertical row of four scars, whereas in *Ilyocypris* there are five scars. In the latter form, an arcuate row of four scars is present, but on the posterior concave side of these scars is an important fifth and largest scar. The long radial-pore canals of *Limnocythere* traverse a broad, fused duplicature. Those of *Ilyocypris* are short and join a distinct vestibule with the outer margin. Unfortunately, both muscle scars and radial-pore canals are frequently obliterated in the present poorly preserved fauna, but it is unlikely that *Ilyocypris* has been overlooked during the present study. Because species of *Limnocythere* prefer lacustrine to oligohaline habitats and those of *Ilyocypris* are more frequently found in running waters, there are important paleoecologic inferences to be made from proper identification of these two forms.

Past workers with *Limnocythere* (Müller, 1900; Ekman, 1914; Brady and Norman, 1889; Schäfer, 1953; Staplin, 1963) have identified a number of phenetic variants which some called species and others considered as somatic differences. Taxonomic importance has been assigned to degree of reticulateness, presence or absence of tubercules, size, and degree of anterior sulcation. Whereas one author might recognize as many as 11 species, another might accept only 3 or 4. Early in the study of this genus, Dahl (1888) thought he could distinguish between the tuberculate type-species *L. inopinata* Baird, 1843, living in the Baltic, and a geographically closely associated smoother form *L. incisa* Dahl, 1874. Several authors, including Klie (1938, p. 150) and Schäfer (1953, p. 364), have considered that most differences in carapace surface sculpture are probably caused by changes in alkalinity or salinity. In the many specimens examined for this report, differences in degree of reticulation and robustness of the carapace were noted, but no strongly tuberculate specimens were seen. The present author recognized no morphologic differences that would not be expected within one population throughout its ecologic range.

No species now described could be positively identified with the specimens of the Rita Blanca lake beds. The group of species encompassing *Limnocythere sanctipatricii* Brady and Robertson, 1869, *L. staplini* Gutentag and Benson, 1962, and possibly *L. friabilis* Benson and MacDonald, 1963, would most readily include the present form.

Candona sp.
(Pl. 21, figs. 3, 5, 7)

Within a few of the apparently carbonaceous, dark layers of the varves examined were many crushed specimens of both sexes, together with many immature specimens, of a species of *Candona*. In original outline these specimens most closely resemble those of *Candona crogmania* Hoff, 1942. Only three specimens were found intact (Pl. 21, fig. 3) of the more than 100 crushed specimens examined. The marginal area and muscle-scar patterns are obscure; however, the subtriangular outline of the female with a truncate posterior, characteristic of *C. crogmania*, is still recognizable. The males (Pl. 21, fig. 5) are presumably of the same species, but their outlines are not as diagnostic.

The specimens of *Candona* are large, elongate to spatulate, very fragile forms with smooth surfaces (unfortunately most are crushed). The males are more reniform and less angular than the females. This genus has a characteristic shape that is easily identifiable.

It is notable that, with a few exceptions (Pl. 21, fig. 7), where specimens of *Candona* were common, those of *Limnocythere* were not. They apparently did not reach the climax of their population development at the same time during varve deposition.

Cyprideis sp.
(Pl. 21, fig. 4; Pl. 22, figs. 4, 5, 6)

Valves of *Cyprideis* were found in not more than 5 of possibly 50 microstratigraphic surfaces examined. They were numerous, but not well preserved. Where they did occur, they were in association with a thicker, more reticulate variant of *Limnocythere*.

Only three adult specimens were found, but comparison of the shape and surfaces of several well-preserved immature specimens with those identified as *Cyprideis salebrosa* Van den Bold, 1963, by Sandberg (1964, p. 144) strongly suggests the presence of this species in the Rita Blanca lake beds. This species is also found in Pliocene (Laverne Formation) sediments in southwestern Kansas (Gutentag and Benson, 1962, then incorrectly identified as *C. littoralis*).

The specimens examined were more robust than those of *Limnocythere* or *Candona*, ovate in shape with a moderately punctuate surface and a faint dorsomedian sulcus in each valve. The immature molts, which are in the vast majority, are broadly rounded at the anterior and tapered toward the blunt posterior. Internal features are observed with difficulty. The marginal area is narrow with a deep but much narrower vestibule. Muscle scars are indicated by raised areas on the inner wall, but could not be observed clearly. A reconstruction is given in Plate 22, figure 5. The upper mandibular scar of these nearly mature molts appeared to be more ovate — as in *Cyprideis mexicana* Sandberg, 1964, than elongate — as in *C. salebrosa* Van den Bold. This observation was made on one probable mature form and could not be considered significant for identification. The hinge has crenulate terminal elements, but the divided median element is obscured by poor preservation.

MODERN ECOLOGY

The literature discussing the environmental distribution of living species of the three genera represented in the Rita Blanca sediments refers primarily to estuarine, lake, and pond bottom-dwellers. An assemblage of abundant limnocytherids, cyprideisids, and candonids, with exclusion of other forms, has been observed only a few times. Klie (1939) found *Cyprideis littoralis* (Brady), 1864 and *Limnocythere africana* Klie, 1939 in Lake Rudolph in Kenya, together with *Heterocypris* and other cyprids. Gutentag and Benson (1962) found *Cyprideis salebrosa, Limnocythere staplini* Gutentag and Benson, and *Candona nyensis* Gutentag and Benson together in the Pliocene (Laverne Formation) deposits of Kansas. These are the only such instances presently known to the author. This combination of forms is apparently unusual and is probably environmentally significant.

Examined collectively, the three genera could represent salinities of oligohaline, possibly mesohaline, to fresh water, or at least strongly alkaline fresh water. All three forms are found in this environment. Some species of *Limnocythere*, such as *L. sanctipatricii*, are generally restricted to fresh-water lakes, except as reported by Swain (1955) from San Antonio Bay and Daday (1903) from a saline lake in Hungary, whereas *L. inopinate* (Baird, 1843) is invariably found in the low saline waters (approximately 3 ‰) of the Baltic–North Sea region (Schäfer, 1953; Hartmann, 1957; Brady and Norman, 1889) and the Black Sea (Klie, 1937). *Limnocythere* has been reported rarely from the marine environment (Brady and Norman, 1889; Brady, 1890). *Cyprideis* on the other hand, is found rarely in fresh-water conditions and is perhaps the most common mesohaline ostracode. It is common in shallow nearshore marine areas, as well as being abundant in lagoons and estuarine situations (Sandberg, 1964).

Within their euryhaline tolerances, *Cyprideis* and *Limnocythere* undergo considerable phenetic changes that are directly correlatable with the salinity gradient. These changes are expressed in the thickness of the carapace wall, robustness of surface texture, and particularly in the development of large nodes. For the purpose of the present study it is unnecessary to review the taxonomic problems that have resulted during the discovery of this relationship. The reader is referred to Sandberg (1964) for a discussion of the influence of environment on the carapace morphology of *Cyprideis*, and to Müller (1900), Ekman (1914), Klie (1938), and Schäfer (1953) for discussions of noding in *Limnocythere*. Van Morkhoven (1962) feels that the problem of phenetic variation in *Limnocythere* is yet unresolved. The preponderance of data, as with *Cyprideis*, seem to suggest very strongly, however, that the linkage of nodosity and salinity change is real.

At present, the consensus is that species of *Cyprideis* become more strongly noded as brackish waters decrease in salinity, and that species of *Limnocythere*, much rarer in these conditions, become more strongly noded and perhaps more reticulate as fresh waters become more saline. In either genus, it is not clear what abnormally increased alkalinity in fresh water does to the nodosity, although Dobbin (1941, p. 186) reported the nodose *Limnocythere inopinata* from "Alkali Lake" in Washington. Swain (1955, p. 613) found *Limnocythere sanctipatricii* living in San Antonio Bay, Texas, in salinities up to and in excess of 10 ‰. He does not describe any gradient of increase in nodosity with increase in salinity, but remarks that Staplin (personal commun. to Swain) thinks this form is "more coarsely pitted (reticulate) than is typical for the species."

Species of all three genera are bottom dwellers. *Candona* is usually a burrower, whereas *Cyprideis* and *Limnocythere* are more commonly surface crawlers. It is significant that active swimmers were not found. This would suggest the absence of abundant aquatic vegetation which serves as a niche for such forms.

The effects on distribution of variation in temperature, both seasonally and with latitude, are not formulated into any patterns that are helpful in the present problem. *Limnocythere* has been observed most frequently in late spring and occasionally in the fall. *Candona* is also seasonal in occurrence, with its greatest abundance usually in the spring generally just before that of *Limnocythere* (from the data of Hoff, 1942, Table 4). The seasonal effects on the distribution of *Cyprideis* are not known.

Geographically, all three genera are world-wide in occurrence. *Candona crogmaniana* Turner, 1894, which closely resembles the form found in the Rita Blanca lake deposits, has been found in ponds in many parts of midcontinental and south-central North America. Most species of *Limnocythere* are restricted geographically, or at least have been made to seem so because of numerous names applied to slightly differing forms. An exception to this is *L. sanctipatricii*, which has been identified in Europe and North America and from two places in Texas (Tressler, 1954; Swain, 1955). *Cyprideis* is common to the estuarine regions the world over. Those species possibly found in the mid-continental region are very common to the lagoons along the coast of the Gulf of Mexico. As Sandberg (1964) suggests, a correlation may exist between the flyways of migratory birds and the distribution of inland occurrences of *Cyprideis*.

PALEOECOLOGICAL INTERPRETATION

The presence of abundant fossil ostracodes belonging to a rare genus concentrated in the light-colored layers of varves and the notable absence of common fresh-water cyprid ostracodes suggest an unusual and repetitive set of environmental circumstances.

The ostracode carapaces do not appear to be sorted according to size or developmental stage. Hundreds of specimens representing immature stages are found together with fewer adult specimens. Hornibrook (1955) noted a similar situation for a species of New Zealand *Limnocythere,* and implied that this is to be expected in a life assemblage. The animals apparently lived and crawled over the surface upon which their fragile carapace remains were deposited. No evidence was found to indicate that they burrowed through the thin varves.

The presence of robust, reticulate specimens of *Limnocythere* with those of *Cyprideis* indicates slightly saline waters, probably from 3 to 5 ‰, or alkaline waters of similar concentration. It is possible that the salinity rose to as much as 10 to 12 ‰, as in San Antonio Bay. But there is as yet no way of estimating the salinity concentration from the relative proportions of *Cyprideis* to *Limnocythere* in a fossil assemblage by analogy with records of modern distribution of these genera. Neither form is nodose, suggesting a paleohabitat of either very saline or nonsaline waters or suggesting that nodosity, although responsive to changes in salinity, is not a predictable indicator of changes in alkalinity. Increases in alkalinity above that level normal for fresh water may not affect nodosity, yet may serve as a barrier for stenohaline fresh-water forms. No experimental information is yet available on this subject.

The great abundance of ostracode specimens of one taxon, such as those of *Limnocythere,* found in the lighter colored portion of the varves without either *Cyprideis* or *Candona,* suggests seasonal blooming just after the spring flood waters have cleared and before the appearance of late bloomers. The absence of *Cyprideis* in most of the varves is to be expected, as this is a form uncommon to fresh-water inland environments. The limited and isolated occurrence of *Candona* suggests a temporal niche difference between it and *Limnocythere.* This hypothesis is strengthened by the occurrence of *Candona* in the darker colored varve layers, with only occasional specimens of *Limnocythere.* Comparison with modern seasonal ostracode distribution indicates this succession of faunas within the varves would have been caused by separate mid-spring and late spring blooms in population.

Candona is usually the most abundant ostracode living on, or crawling on the open bottom area of, lake beds. Its near or total absence in many varves is attributable to the inhospitable surroundings that existed most of the time. That the eggs of all fresh-water ostracodes can endure formidable environmental extremes is well established, so that one would expect these eggs to produce significant populations only when the viable thresholds of environmental change had been passed over. It is obvious that for the Rita Blanca cyprid ostracodes, and in particular candonids, certain limiting minimum thresholds were never attained during many seasons of varve deposition.

CONCLUSIONS

The paleoenvironmental conditions that seem best to satisfy most of the limitations suggested by the ostracodes are those that exist in a moderately large and deep lake in an area of seasonal droughts. Excess evaporation during these times brought salts to the surface of the soil, which was subsequently washed into, and concentrated in, the lake, probably during spring floods.

The superabundance of alkaline material would prohibit all but the most euryhaline fresh-water ostracodes from living on the bottom of the deep lake areas where varves might form and be preserved. The coincidence of the lake on the route of birds flying north from brackish lagoons on the Gulf of Mexico provided a stock of normally brackish-water-inhabiting ostracodes which became conspicuous when the other forms reached their upper salinity tolerance. The predominance of *Limnocythere* is a consequence of its salinity tolerance over that of other fresh-water ostracodes.

The occurrence of the ostracode valves in association with certain types of laminae reflects the seasonality of the fresh water ostracodes along with that of lacustrine deposition. Few species live more than the short spring or summer period of optimum environmental conditions for which they have become adapted. Their eggs lie dormant during the unfavorable parts of the year. Spring and early summer population blooms yielded accumulations of dead carapaces representing a mixture of growth stages. Vertical stratigraphic separation of fossil populations of *Limnocythere* and *Candona* reflects a commonly observed temporal difference in the bloom climaxes of the different species during those years which produced more tolerant and fresher waters.

In Part IV of this report, Anderson and Kirkland postulate, among other possibilities, that the lake might have been chemically stratified with a stagnant hypolimnion in order to preserve the varves. The presence of ostracodes would not negate this theory, as they are frequently found to inhabit and flourish in conditions unfavorable to other forms of life. The nature of the ostracode assemblage and its cyclic occurrence strongly suggests unusual chemical conditions in Rita Blanca lake.

REFERENCES CITED

Benson, R. H., and MacDonald, H. C., 1963, Postglacial (Holocene) ostracodes from Lake Erie: Kans. Univ. Paleont. Contr., Arthropoda, art. 3, p. 1–26, pls. 1–4, figs. 1–8

Brady, G. S., 1890, On ostracode collected by H. B. Brady, Esq., LLD., FRS., in the South Sea Islands: Royal Soc. Edinberg Trans., v. 35, no. 14, p. 489–525, pls. I–IV

Brady, G. S., and Norman, A. M., 1889, A monograph of the marine and freshwater Ostracoda of the North Atlantic and of North-western Europe; Sec. 1, Podocopa: Royal Dublin Soc. Sci. Trans., ser. 2, v. 4, p. 63–270, pls. 8–23

Brady, G. S., and Robertson, D., 1869, Notes of a week's dredging in the west of Ireland: Annals Mag. Nat. Hist., ser. 4, v. 3, p. 353–374, pls. 18–22

Daday, E., 1903, Mikroskopische Süsswassertiere der Umgebung von Balaton: Zool. Jahrb. Abt. Syst. Geographie Biologie, v. 19, no. 1, p. 37–98, pls. 5, 6

Dahl, Friedrich, 1888, Die cytheriden der westlichen Ostsee: Zool. Jahrb. Syst. Geographie u. Biologie, v. 3, no. 4, p. 597–638, pls. 16–19

Dobbin, C. N., 1941, Fresh-water Ostracoda from Washington and other western localities: Wash. Univ. Pub. Biology, v. 4, no. 3, p. 175–246

Ekman, Sven, 1914, Beiträge zur Kenntnis der schwedischen Süsswasser-Ostracoden: Zool. Bidrag Uppsala, v. 3, p. 1–36, 80 figs.

Gutentag, E. D., and Benson, R. H., 1962, Neogene (Plio-Pleistocene) Freshwater ostracodes from the Central High Plains: Kans. Geol. Survey Bull. 157, p. 1–60, pls. 1, 2

Hartmann, G., 1957, Neue Funde von Muschelkrebsen (Ostracoda) im Gebiet der Nordseeküste und der Kieler Bucht: Schr. Naturw. Vereins Schleswig-Holstein, v. 28, no. 2, p. 103–111, pls. 1–17

Hoff, C. C., 1942, The ostracods of Illinois: Ill. Biol. Mon., Univ. Ill. Press, v. 19, no. 1–2, p. 1–196

Hornibrook, N. deB., 1955, Ostracoda in the deposits of Pyramid Valley swamp: Christchurch, New Zealand, Canterbury Mus. Rec., v. 6, no. 4, p. 267–278, 34 figs.

Klie, W., 1937, Ostracoden und Harpacticoiden aus brackigen Gewässern an der bulgarischen Küste des Schwarzen Meeres: Metteil Königl. Naturwiss. Inst. Sofia-Bulgar, v. X, p. 1–42

—— 1938, Krebstiere oder Crustacea, III, Ostracoda, Muschelkrebse, in Dahl Die Tierwelt Deutschlands und der angrenzenden Meeresteile, v. 34, pt. 3, p. 1–230

—— 1939, Ostracoden aus dem Kenia-Gebier, vornehmlich von desser Hochgebirge: Internat. Rev. gesamten. Hydrobiologie u. Hydrographie, v. 39, p. 99–161

Müller, G. W., 1900, Deutchland Süsswasser-Ostracoden: Zooligica, v. 12, no. 30, p. 1–112

Sandberg, P. A., 1964, The ostracod genus *Cyprideis* in the Americas: Stockholm, Contr. in Geology, v. XII, p. 1–178, pls. 1–23

Sars, G. O., 1925, Ostracoda; Cypridae (concluded), Cytheridae (part): An account of the Crustacea of Norway: Bergen, Bergen Mus., p. 137–176, pls. LVX–LXXX

Schäfer, H. W., 1953, Über Meeres-und Brackwasserostracoden aus dem deutschen Küstengebier mit: 2 Mitteilungen über die Ostracodenfauna Griechenlands: Hydrobiologie, v. 5, no. 4, p. 351–389, 15 figs.

Staplin, F. L., 1963, Pleistocene Ostracoda of Illinois, pt. II: Jour. Paleontology, v. 37, p. 1164–1203

Swain, F. M., 1955, Ostracoda of San Antonio Bay, Texas: Jour. Paleontology, v. 29, p. 561–646

Tressler, W. L., 1954, Fresh water Ostracoda from Texas and New Mexico: Jour. Washington Acad. Sci., v. 44, no. 5, p. 138–149

van Morkhoven, F. P., 1962, Post-Paleozoic Ostracoda, their morphology, taxonomy, and economic use: Amsterdam, Elsevier Pub. Co., v. i, II, 204 p.

Aquatic Insects of the Rita Blanca Lake Deposits

JAMES E. SUBLETTE

Eastern New Mexico University, Portales, New Mexico

INTRODUCTION

The sediments that accumulated in the profundal zone of Rita Blanca Lake entombed a "death assemblage." It is probable that the remains of most of the aquatic species of animals, and for certain all of the aquatic insects, present in these sediments were transported from the overlying mixolimnion of this meromictic lake, not from animals living *in situ*. The most conclusive proof of this lies in the nature of the animal remains themselves:

(1) There is only a single larval head capsule among several hundred examples of the family Chironomidae, and this was lying adjacent to a pupal exuvia. If Chironomids had inhabited the monimolimnion, the head capsules would have been readily detected. That they were not overlooked is evidenced by valves of ostracodes, which have been recovered by the thousands. These valves were frequently smaller than the single larval head recovered. The one head capsule found is to be explained by observations of living species: as larvae undergo ecdysis, not infrequently a larval exuvia will fail to separate from the pupa but will remain attached to it and will be transported along with the pupa to its ultimate fate.

(2) A bulk of the remains of aquatic insects is in the form of exuvae of pupae and naiads. Next in abundance are pupae and naiads (some showing partial ecdysis) and partially decomposed adults.

Pupal exuvaie are delicate, easily fragmented evidences of past life. They could have persisted and have been preserved only in (1) the absence of any macroscopic life on the profundal lake floor, which could have quickly fragmented any remains, and (2) the absence of water circulation. The aquatic fauna is characterized by a general paucity of species, notable absence or rarity of three major groups normally found in littoral and sublittoral zones of lakes — Ephemeroptera, Hemiptera, and Coleoptera (*see* chapter by Werner, this report) — and the relative abundance of two species, *Chironomus kirklandi* new species and a presumptive species (unnamed) of Libellulidae.

SYSTEMATIC DESCRIPTIONS AND ANNOTATED LIST
OF SPECIES AND GROUPS

Order ODONATA
Suborder ANISOPTERA
Family LIBELLULIDAE
Sp.
(Pl. 12, figs. 1, 2, 3)

This family was represented by an apparent species which was one of the most common aquatic insects in the Rita Blanca lake deposits. Unfortunately, diagnostic features are not sufficiently discernable to assign a scientific name. Represented by 17 collections.

COLLECTION: 51, 120, 133, 169, 205, 318, 391, B-108, B-129, 13-137, B-149, B-152, B-191, B-215, B-223, B-308, 25 R.C., 40 R.C.

Family AESHNIDAE

The family assignment is problematical inasmuch as the diagnostic features at the family level are not discernible. Needless to say, a scientific name assignment would be meaningless. However, general body shape and some indication of wing pads would strongly suggest this family placement. This was the second most abundant group of Odonata represented by six collections and four collections of the same probable group.

COLLECTION: 134, 159, 241, 311, 323, 448, B-284, JE-404, P-60-68.

Suborder ZYGOPTERA
Family ?COENAGRIONIDAE
(Pl. 12, fig. 4)

Since gills and labium are not visible on the single specimen, this could just as well be Lestidae.

COLLECTION: 328.

Order TRICHOPTERA
Family ?MOLANNIDAE (SERICOSTOMATIDAE)
Pl. 13, fig. 1)

Identification based on larval cases is extremely difficult. The general appearance will fit either of the families listed above. Rare occurrence in the deposits.

COLLECTION: 432, JE 381.

Order DIPTERA
Family CULICIDAE
Culex sp.
(Pl. 13, fig. 2)

COLLECTION: 181.

Aedes sp.

Specific identification of recent forms is based primarily on scale patterns, color features, and genitalic characteristics. Generic identifications in the mosquitoes are of little significance in attempting to reconstruct paleoecology. We must assume a broad ecological valence as in neoecology. Rare occurrence in the deposits.

Family CHIRONOMIDAE

The abundant material of this family from the Rita Blanca beds is in a poor state of preservation. In no instance were wings preserved in a state sufficient to render the venation discernable, nor were details of genitalia and leg spurs visible, except in one species which is described below. Thus, it is difficult even to identify subfamilies for much of the material.

One species of Chironomini was abundantly represented in the material in the larval, pupal, and adult stages. It is sufficiently preserved to enable the following description to be given.

Subfamily CHIRONOMINAE
Chironomus (Chironomus) kirklandi Sublette n. sp.
(Pl. 13, figs. 3, 4, 5; Pl. 14, figs. 1, 2, 3, 4, 5; Pl. 15, figs. 1, 2, 3, 4)

Holotype male, in the collection of the U.S. National Museum, no. 66660. Collected from the Rita Blanca lake beds, near Channing, Texas, Rita Blanca deposits, late Pliocene or early Pleistocene, collection no. 303, Douglas W. Kirkland.

Ground color of head and thorax brown: thoracic vittae, postnotum, and mesosternum blackish brown. Abdomen largely blackish brown but with a narrow apical lighter band on each segment; tergites with each bristle aveolus lighter in color forming a conspicuous punctuate pattern.

Eyes with dorsal extensions, as is characteristic of most members of the subfamily (cf. Pl. 13, fig. 3, paratype ♂). Frontal tubercles not evident. Palpus four segmented; antennal length 1.15 mm.

Prothorax normally developed, collarlike, reaching apex of mesonotum; notch not clearly apparent, but probably present. Dorsolateral bristles in conspicuous multiple rows; other bristles not evident.

Fore tibia with a low, rounded scale typical of the genus; fore tarsus not bearded; middle and hind legs missing. Proportions of foreleg:

F	Ti	Ta1	Ta2	Ta3	Ta4	Ta5	Leg ratio
80	81	82	45	32	26	15	1.00

Genital capsule massive (cf. Pl. 14, figs. 1, 2) forming a slight terminal enlargement very similar to *Chironomus noctivaga* (Kieffer) (= *taurica* Tshernorskij, new synonomy); entire capsule blackened, inferior appendages somewhat lighter; dististyles distinctively shaped. Inferior appendages long, reaching about two-thirds of the way to the tip of the dististyles. Anal point broad; superior appendage obscured (Pl. 13, figs. 4 [holotype male] and 5 [paratype male]).

Allotype female, in the collection of the U.S. National Museum (Pl. 14, fig. 1); on a slab with a male and female (faint) paratype (collection no. 176). There are also faint fragments of pupal exuviae on the slab.

Similar to the male in size, coloration and general morphology. Wing length 5.10 mm; wing obscured, except for anterior veins which are dark brown. Body length 6.44 mm. Foreleg proportions:

F	Ti	Ta1	Ta2	Ta3	Ta4	Ta5	Leg ratio
	102	110	55	43	30	17	1.08

Middle and hind legs obscured.

Genital lamellae not discernable due to dorsoventral flattening of abdomen of all specimens.

PARATYPE MALES: Wing length 4.00 mm (3); total length 5.77–7.10, mean 6.43 mm (4); foreleg ratio, 1.00–1.15, mean 1.06 (7); middle leg ratio, 0.43–0.45, mean 0.44 (4); hind leg ratio, 0.45–0.53, mean 0.48 (5); antennal ratio 4.11, 4.44 (2).

PARATYPE FEMALES: Wing length, 4.66, 5.33 mm (2); total length 5.11–6.13 mm (3); foreleg ratio 1.00, 1.05 (2).

PARATYPES: 27 males, 17 females, about 210 pupae and pupal exuviae, many fragmentary (Pl. 14, fig. 4; Pl. 15, figs. 1–4). In the collections of the University of New Mexico Museum, U.S. National Museum, Philadelphia Academy of Natural Sciences, and author's collection.

LARVA: Described from a single larval head capsule associated on the same small slab with pupae, pupal exuviae, and an adult male. Head capsule yellowish with the venter dark brown and the tips of the mandible, labial plate, and occiput black. All details of the head obscured, except the labial plate (Pl. 14, fig. 5) which is extremely similar to other species of *Chironomus* (s.s.). Head length 0.80 mm.

PUPA: Described from many exuviae, fully developed pupae, and pupae which partially completed ecdysis (Pl. 14, fig. 4; Pl. 15, figs. 1–4).

Total length 9.32–11.54, mean 10.14 mm (6). Cephalic tubercles small and acutely tipped; bristle not visible; respiratory organs apparently not preserved. Thorax and abdomen blackened; chaetotaxy of abdomen not discernable. Spur of posterior-lateral margin of segment VIII and anal fin shown in Pl. 14, fig. 4; anal fin with about 55 fringe bristles.

This species is clearly distinguishable from extant Nearctic Chironomini on the basis of the distinctive male genitalia. It closely resembles the Paleaarctic *Chironomus* (*Halliella*) *noctivaga* (Kieffner). Leg ratios, palpal proportions, and genitalic features however, indicate this to be a distinct species.

The subgenus *Halliella* Kieffner of the genus *Chironomus* (*Halliella* originally proposed as a genus) has as its principal diagnostic feature the presence of shortened, usually 3-segmented palpi. On this basis, the foregoing species must be considered a *Chironomus* (s.s.) since it has normal length, 4-segmented palpi. Yet, in all features except this, it is extremely similar to *Chironomus* (*Halliella*) *noctivage* (Kieffner). It must be concluded that *C. kirklandi* new species represents a species population at the point of divergence between *Chironomus* (s.s.) and *Chironomus* (*Halliella*). It is questionable whether *Halliella* should be maintained as a separate subgenus of *Chironomus*, since in all stages it so closely resembles *Chironomus* (ss.) (cf. Botnaruic and Albu, 1958). All known species of *Chironomus* (*Halliella*) are halophilic. Since many lines of evidence point to Rita Blanca Lake as having been a saline meromictic lake, we must assume *Chironomus kirklandi* new species had an ecology similar to extant species of *Chironomus* (*Halliella*).

COLLECTION: 303 holotype, U.S. National Museum; 176 allotype and paratype, U.S. National Museum; 26, 54, 55, 71, 153, 170, 164, 183, 193, 198, 213, 223, 248, 279, 282, 286, 288, 292, 299, 301, 312, 326, 327, 331, 422, 429, 431, 437, 438, 446, 455, 479, B-107, B-112, B-136, B-138, B-145, B-159, B-163, B-166, B-167, B-237, B-238, B-259, B-291, B-292, B-301, C-2, C-4, C-12, JE-382, JE-384, 272A, 6B, 166B, 295B, 443B.

Chironomus (*?Endochironomus*) sp.

COLLECTION: 437.

?Tanytarsus sp.

COLLECTION: 250, 289.

Subfamily ?ORTHOCLADIINAE
(Pl. 15, figs. 5, 6)

COLLECTION: 82, 105, 151, 200, 206, 207, 217, 222, 231, 252, 263, 389, 472, B-128, B-139, B-172, B-205, B-245, C-27.

Subfamily ?TANYPODINAE
(Pl. 16, figs. 1, 2)

COLLECTION: B-209, C-196.

The preceding four identifications are based more on general impression than on precise taxonomic criteria. An experienced taxonomist will frequently sort specimens to "apparent species" before actually consulting delimiting characteristics. Such was the identification here. Most precise taxonomic characteristics are missing so this impression of apparent species must serve as the only means of identification.

COMPARISON OF THE AQUATIC INSECT FAUNA OF RITA BLANCA LAKE WITH MEROMICTIC LAKES

Noncirculating alkaline or saline lakes have been studied rather infrequently in the past. Of those reported in the literature, still fewer have presented

Species or group	Rita Blanca Lake	Green Lake (Eggleton, 1956)	Austrian lakes (Findenegg, 1953, 1955) See Weissen-Worther-Millstatter		
Odonata	X	X	X	..	..
Libellulidae	X	..	X	..	..
Aeschidae	X	..	..	..	..
?Coenagrionidae	X	..	..	..	..
Megaloptera	..	..	..	..	X
Sialidae	..	..	..	..	X
Sialis	..	..	..	..	X
Hemiptera	..	X	..	..	..
Trichoptera	X	X	..	..	..
?Mollanidae	X	..	..	..	..
Coleoptera	..	X	X	..	..
Diptera	X	X	X	X	X
Culicidae	..	..	..	..	..
Aedes sp.	X	..	..	..	..
Culex sp.	X	..	..	..	..
Chironomidae	..	..	..	..	..
Chironomini	X	..	X	X	X
Chironomus bathophilus	..	..	X	X	X
Chironomus kirklandi	X	..	..	..	..
Chironomus (Cryptochironomus) defectus gr.	..	..	X	..	X
Chironomus (Dicrotendipes)	..	..	..	..	..
Stictochironomus sp.	..	..	X	X	X
Chironomus (?Endochironomus) sp.	X	..	..	..	..
Polypedilum sp.	..	..	X	X	..
Microtendipes sp.	..	..	..	X	X
Tanytarsus sp.	?X	..	..	X	X
Tanytarsus genuinus gr. sp.	..	..	..	..	X
Paratanytarsus sp.	..	..	X	X	..
?*Tanytarsus* sp.	X	..	..	..	..
Tanypodinae	?X	..	X	X	..
Procladius pectinatus	..	..	X	X	..
Orthocladiinae	?X	..	X	..	..
Orthocladius lenzianus	..	..	X	..	..
Prodiamesa sp.	..	..	..	..	X
Ceratopogonidae	..	..	..	..	X
Ceratopogon sp.	..	..	..	..	X

detailed studies of the benthos. In the Nearctic Region only the report of Eggleton (1956) is available, while in the Palearctic Region only the work of Findenegg (1953; 1955) presents detailed descriptions of the fauna.

Table 8 presents a comparison of the insect benthos of Rita Blanca lake with three meromictic lakes. Only rather general systematics were employed in Eggleton's study; consequently, comparisons are not too meaningful. Also, the fact of meromixis may not be critical to the distribution of the insects. While Findenegg's reports were detailed, few specific faunal elements are common to both Palearctic and Nearctic Regions. Hence, precise comparisons of the Rita Blanca benthic fauna must await additional neolimnological investigations of Nearctic meromictic lakes in which precise systematics are employed.

ACKNOWLEDGMENTS

Several specialists have assisted in the identification of the material described. I should like to thank Dr. H. H. Ross for his identification of the Trichoptera, Dr. W. W. Wirth for the Culicidae, and Dr. M. J. Westfall, the Odonata. I have incorporated several of Dr. Westfall's comments (in litt.) into the brief discussion of the Odonata.

REFERENCES CITED

Botnaruic, N., and Albu, P., 1958, *Halliella taurica* Tshernovskij, eine zirkumpontische Art (Diptera: Tendipedidae): Beitr. zur Entomologie, v. 8 (5/6), p. 697–710

Eggleton, F. E., 1956, Limnology of a Meromictic, interglacial, plunge-basin lake: Am. Micros. Soc. Trans. Soc., v. 75, p. 334–378

Findenegg, Ingo, 1953, Kärntner Seen naturkundlich betrachtet: Carinthia II, Sonderheft, v. 15, p. 5–101

—— 1955, Die profundal fauna der Kärntner Seen und ihr Verhältnis zu deren Trophiezustand.: Ist. Ital. Idrobiol. Supp. 8, p. 121–140

Terrestrial Insects of the
Rita Blanca Lake Deposits

FLOYD G. WERNER

University of Arizona,[1] Tucson, Arizona

INTRODUCTION

In the following account of the terrestrial insects many of the specimens are only tentatively identified, and then often only to the family or subfamily level. All the terrestrial insects recovered from the deposits for which some affinities could be determined are included, with the exception of the weevils which are treated in a separate article by E. L. Sleeper. Unfortunately, some of the specimens of terrestrial insects were lost in shipment after they had been described and photographed.

The insects identified are only of moderate value in helping to clarify the climatic or ecological setting of the lake. The identifications to group are too general to be of value, and most of the species that could be identified with certainty are widespread. The insects that occur in greatest abundance were probably associated with the pond, whereas some of the individual specimens may have entered by accident. The three meloid beetles might indicate that the surrounding country was mostly grassland. There is a conspicuous absence of wood-boring insects; one might expect a few of the adults if they were abundant.

[1]University of Arizona, Agricultural Experiment Station, Journal article no. 1108.

SYSTEMATIC DESCRIPTIONS

Order HEMIPTERA
Suborder GYMNOCERATA
Superfamily TINGOIDEA
Family TINGIDAE
Sp.
(Pl. 16, fig. 3)

One of the narrow forms; body 3.7 mm long. Family identification possible because of reticulations of anterior wings shown along sides of body. The wings seem to narrow anteriorly so that they barely reach beyond the body, but this portion may have been lost in preservation.

COLLECTION: C-3.

Superfamily LYGAEOIDEA
Family LYGAEIDAE
Nysius? sp.
(Pl. 16, figs. 4, 6)

What seems to be a single species is represented by a rather large number of specimens. Only 477 is clearly adult, with wings showing; this specimen is 3.9 mm in body length. Sample 173-201-B150 is one piece, about 5 square inches, with dozens of individuals and some associated plant materials. JE 378 to JE 367 have smaller assemblages of nymphs and plant material. The rest are single specimens. The presence of such assemblages suggests that the nymphs were feeding on plants (grasses?) actually growing in the water or close to it. The family identification is based on the wing venation and presence of ocelli in many of the specimens, of the genus on head shape and size, in particular. Recent species are often gregarious in the nymphal stage.

COLLECTION: 477, 173-201-B150, JE 378, B192-B173, 66, B252, 60, 89, JE 367, 83, 219 R. C., 116, B269, B203, 67.

HEMIPTERA, position uncertain
Sp.

About 4.8 mm body length. This specimen has 4-segmented antennae and 3-segmented tarsi, so it must be Hemiptera. Antennal segment 2 is enlarged, and probably hollowed out on one side. This characteristic does not fit anything in the University of Arizona collection but is something like that found in the males of some Miridae; these are much smaller.

COLLECTION: 148.

Sp.
(Pl. 16, fig. 5)

Very obviously Hemiptera, because of the conformation of abdomen and head. Body 5.9 mm long. This is probably either Lygaeidae or Corizidae, but there is no way of telling without wings. It could also be Coreidae.

COLLECTION: JE 397.

Sp.

Because of the large size, about 13 mm, and slender shape, this specimen would be easily assigned if it had wings showing. The most likely possibilities are Lygaeidae (*Lygaeus* or *Oncopeltus*), but Pyrrhocoridae (*Dysdercus*) or Corizidae (*Leptocoris*) are also possibilities.

COLLECTION: B170.

Sp.

Probably Lygaeidae, cf. *Ligyrocoris*. Male, 7.3 mm long, with slightly swollen anterior femora.

COLLECTION: 237.

Order HOMOPTERA
Suborder AUCHENORRHYNCHA
Family CICADELLIDAE
Sp. cf. Deltocephalinae
(Pl. 16, fig. 7)

Size 4.3 mm and 3.9 mm. Both specimens clearly Cicadellidae and show the same kind of darkening near the wing veins. B241 shows some markings on the frontal area of the head.

COLLECTION: JE 347, B241.

Sp.
(Pl. 17, fig. 3)

Two specimens on this piece seem to be the same. There is a little piece of wing showing on each, and the markings of the previous species seem to be absent. Length 3.7 mm.

COLLECTION: 107.

Sp.

Size 3.8 mm and 4.1 mm. These seem to be dark, and show no wings. The front of the head could be more blunt than in the previous two, but there is little to go on.

COLLECTION: 270, 102.

Spp.

There are probably several species involved, because of the variation in size; no specimens show wings; JE 395, 5 plus mm; 173, several specimens at about 5 mm; B280, 6.0 mm; B122, 6.6 mm; and B204, 7.5 mm. B122 shows the characteristic hind legs very well. The specimens on 173 are mixed with the *Nysius*? sp. that are so numerous on that piece.

COLLECTION: JE 395, 173, B280, B122, B204.

Superfamily FULGOROIDEA
Family AREOPODIDAE?
Sp.

While the antennae do not show, the whole conformation of the body is of a fulgoroid, and the hind legs are not greatly enlarged. Length 5.4 mm to tip of wings.

COLLECTION: 75.

Order COLEOPTERA
Suborder ADEPHAGA
Family CARABIDAE
Sp., cf. *Selenophorus*
(Pl. 17, fig. 1)

Two specimens measure 5.3 mm. The divided first abdominal sternum is visible in both; the unnumbered specimen shows enlarged trochanters on the hind legs, clearly walking legs, and full-sized last segment of maxillary palpus. Both show a dark body and pale legs.

COLLECTION: 214, and unnumbered.

B302 is also 5.3 mm long, and looks like the others. It shows filiform antennae and carabidlike mandibles: 88 and 493 are similar but pale, show nothing that could be used for family placement.

Small carabid beetles would probably be found on muddy shores. The first three specimens look enough alike to belong to the same species.

COLLECTION: 88 and 493, B302.

Suborder POLYPHAGA
Superfamily STAPHYLINOIDEA
Family STAPHYLINIDAE
Sp., *Aleocharinae*?
(Pl. 16, fig. 8)

Length 2.8 mm. This specimen clearly belongs to this family. The slightly thickened antennae and form of the prothorax suggest *Aleocharinae*.
COLLECTION: C-10.

Superfamily CUCUJOIDEA
Family COCCINELLIDAE
Hippodamia convergens?

This specimen is assigned to family on the basis of shape and conformation of thorax and legs. There are few living species in its size, about 5.6 mm in length. JE 354 shows markings on the elytra that are consistent with *H. convergens,* and of no other species now found in the general area. The elytral spots are somewhat larger than they are in recent specimens in the University of Arizona collection.
COLLECTION: JE 354-JE 356.

Superfamily MELOOIDEA
Family MELOIDAE
Lytta sp.
(Pl. 17, fig. 5)

Specimen number 433–481 shows coloration clearly: elytra, mesothorax, metathorax, and abdomen black; head, prothorax, and legs contrastingly pale. Antennae missing, but mouth parts obvious and of chewing type. Elytra distinctly scabrous. Length 13.8 mm, of elytra 8.0 mm. 36–68 is much less complete but well preserved. A small portion of metathoracic wing is visible in both; it is fuscous. 68 shows one tarsal claw clearly, lying along the edge of the metathoracic wing; it shows the deep cleft into two blades. This species is assigned to *Lytta* on the basis of the simple mouthparts, cleft and not combed tarsal claws, mostly glabrous body and strongly contrasting color pattern. I do not believe that it can be assigned to any living species. The entirely pale legs, prothorax, and head are unique. *Lytta (Paralytta) deserticola* Horn comes closest, but has some black at apices of femora and on tibiae and tarsi. This species ranges to the west, from southwestern Utah to Sonora and east to the Rio Grande in New Mexico. The elytra are very much like those of the fossil sp.
COLLECTION: 433–481, 36–68.

Epicauta sp.

This specimen can be assigned to Meloidae on the basis of shape and by the characteristic conformation of the mesothorax shown in JE 403. It is assigned to *Epicauta* on the basis of the large number of small punctures on head, prothorax and elytra, an indication of rather dense pubescence. The color was probably uniformly brown. Length 15.0 mm, of elytra about 10 mm.
COLLECTION: JE 399–JE 403.

Superfamily SCARABAEOIDEA
Family SCARABAEIDAE
Sp., cf. *Diplotaxis*
(Pl. 17, fig. 4)

Teeth on anterior tibiae, projecting and emarginate clypeus and oval shape indicate Scarabaeidae and probably this genus. Length about 9.1 mm; color uniform, probably dark brown.
COLLECTION: B100–B120.

Superfamily CHRYSOMELOIDEA
Family CHRYSOMELIDAE
Sp., Chrysomelinae cf. *Phaedon*

Shows fine detail on underside. Hind coxae widely separated, middle coxae moderately separated, femora all stout. Antennae filiform. The size and absence of any sign of pale markings indicate *Phaedon*. Living species of the genus eat leaves of *Salix*. Length 4.5 mm.

COLLECTION: B232.

Disonycha sp., Halticinae

Assignable to subfamily on enlarged hind femora, to genus on size and color pattern. Elytra (86) with a narrow margin and broad discal stripe dark, otherwise pale; femora (C7) pale with apical third dark. C7 also shows the prothorax to be pale. Length 5.7 mm.

COLLECTION: 86–C7.

Superfamily CURCULIONOIDEA
Family CURCULIONIDAE

See paper on fossil weevils by E. L. Sleeper, this report.

Order DIPTERA
Suborder NEMATOCERA

See paper on aquatic insects by J. E. Sublette, this report.

Suborder BRACHYCERA
Family BOMBYLIIDAE
Sp.
(Pl. 17, figs. 6, 7)

Wing on right side partly embedded, but visible when specimen wet. Veins R_{2+3} and R_4 curve forward and reach anterior margin; anal cell seems to be open at wing margin. There is no indication of color pattern on the wings. The wing venation seems to be similar to that of *Bombylius*. Length of body 5 mm, of proboscis 2.2 mm.

COLLECTION: B130.

Suborder CYCLORRHAPHA
Series ASCHIZA
Family SYRPHIDAE
Sp., cf. *Syrphus*
(Pl. 18, figs. 1, 2)

The conspicuous abdominal markings and the wing venation permit identification to subfamily Syrphinae. There are several genera close to *Syrphus*. The larvae are predaceous on aphids.

COLLECTION: B264–B303.

Series SCHIZOPHORA
Section ACALYPTRATAE
Sp.
(Pl. 17, fig. 2)

Some wing venation is visible on this specimen. Body length about 5 mm.

COLLECTION: 335.

Section CALYPTRATAE
(Pl. 18, fig. 3)

Length 7 mm. This is a stocky fly with bristles on head, thorax, abdomen, and legs. The principal possibilities are the families Tachinidae, Calliphoridae, Muscidae, and Sarcophagidae.

COLLECTION: B226–B273.

Order HYMENOPTERA
Suborder APOCRITA
Superfamily ICHNEUMONOIDEA
Family ICHNEUMONIDAE
Sp.
(Pl. 18, fig. 4)

This specimen, a female, is remarkably well preserved, even showing the sculpture of the side of the thorax and propodeum. Body length 7.5 mm without ovipositor, of which 2.4 mm is visible.

COLLECTION: B232.

Sp.
(Pl. 18, figs. 5, 6)

Body all dark, and legs pale. Length of body about 9 mm without ovipositor, which is broken off almost at the base.

COLLECTION: 280.

ICHNEUMONOIDEA, position uncertain
Sp.
(Pl. 18, fig. 7)

Assigned here on shape and exserted ovipositor. Probably family Braconidae. Body length 4.4 mm without ovipositor, of which 2.6 mm is showing.

COLLECTION: C-6.

Superfamily SCOLIOIDEA
Family TIPHIIDAE?
Sp., cf. *Myzinum*

Female about 13 mm. Rather incomplete. Wings on left side with costal cell and with hymenopterous arrangement of veins. One leg showing on right side stout and apparently fossorial.

COLLECTION: 171.

Family FORMICIDAE
DORYLINAE–ECITONINI or CHELIOMYRMICINI
Sp.
(Pl. 19, fig. 1)

A beautifully preserved male. Dr. M. R. Smith (U.S. National Museum) and Mr. R. W. Taylor (Harvard University) have examined the photograph of this specimen. Both agree to the assignment to tribe, but neither to a closer identification. Army ants have been recorded from 40° N. lat in the United States, but are probably more numerous in the South and Southwest.

COLLECTION: 258.

MYRMICINAE
Sp.
(Pl. 19, fig. 2)

Seems to have 2 petiolar segments and a rather firm gaster. The body color is darker than in the Formicinae specimens. There is an indication of wings, but not enough for identification. Length about 10.5 mm.

COLLECTION: 480.

FORMICINAE
Sp.
(Pl. 19, fig. 5)

Length about 10 mm. This is clearly an alate ant, with elbowed antennae. There appears to be a single petiole. The mandibles show well. 78-111 is similar and may be same. It shows elbowed antennae and oval compound eyes.

COLLECTION: 94–C19, 78–111.

FORMICIDAE, position uncertain

Sp.

Has general shape of an ant. Length about 9 mm.

COLLECTION: B119.

Superfamily VESPOIDEA

Family POMPILIDAE

Sp.

(Pl. 19, fig. 4; Pl. 20, fig. 1)

The long tibial spurs and general conformation indicate the family. Body all dark, wings fuscous, antennae heavy. Body length 9.5 mm.

COLLECTION: JE 340–JE 357.

Superfamily APOIDEA

Sp.

(Pl. 19, fig. 3)

Surely a bee, because of heavy body, heavy and densely pubescent hind legs and heavy abdomen. Forepart of body, probably including mesothorax, missing. Length of fragment 12.5 mm. Because of size and the kind of hind legs, looks like Apidae-Anthophorinae.

COLLECTION: B218.

Sp.

Also surely a bee, and it has the front wings hairy, at least near the anterior margin. Head missing. Length 10.8 mm.

COLLECTION: 257.

Order HYMENOPTERA, position uncertain

Sp.

(Pl. 20, fig. 2)

This specimen has a constricted abdomen and a petiole, but the antennae are not elbowed. There is an indication of wings. Length 3.8 mm. Might be a male ant.

COLLECTION: 35 R.C.

Sp.

Abdomen constricted; antennae not elbowed; wings indicated. Could be a male ant. Length 4.3 mm.

COLLECTION: 447.

Sp.

Has aspect of a small sphecoid wasp, such as *Astata*. It has what looks like large compound eyes, and the slender antennae are inserted near each other on the front. Length 2.5 mm.

COLLECTION: 56.

INSECTA, position uncertain

Sp.

Might be a leafhopper.

COLLECTION: JE 346, B121, B300, 421, B222.

Sp.

Small Hemiptera?

COLLECTION: B261, B200.

Sp.

Hymenoptera?

COLLECTION: 101.

Sp.

COLLECTION: 132.

Nematocerous fly, cf. Tipulidae?

Sp.

Homoptera-Aphididae. Right antenna looks like it.
COLLECTION: 79.

Sp.
(Pl. 20, fig. 3)

Leg, beautifully preserved, Tarsi 5-segmented. Rather hairy and spiny. Terminal region missing. Could be Diptera, Hymenoptera, possibly Coleoptera.
COLLECTION: 146.

Two New Cleoninae from the Rita Blanca Lake Deposits (Coleoptera: Curculionidae)

Elbert L. Sleeper[1]

California State College at Long Beach

INTRODUCTION

The following descriptions of new species of *Cleonus* are drawn from material submitted to the author for study by Roger Y. Anderson and Douglas W. Kirkland. They represent material from the Rita Blanca Lake deposits near Channing (Hartley County), Texas.

So far as can be determined these represent the first records of weevils, and particularly the genus *Cleonus* from the Pleistocene in the United States. Scudder (1900) described six species of weevil (no Cleoninae) from the Toronto Pleistocene of Canada.

SYSTEMATIC DESCRIPTIONS

Order COLEOPTERA
Family Curculionidae
Cleonus (*Cleonidius*) *ritablancaensis*, n. sp.
(Pl. 20, fig. 5)

Holotype: Texas, Hartley County, Mustang Draw (Rita Blanca lake deposits). Lateral aspect and not a complete fossil. Collection no. 98. Length of preserved parts 7.5 mm, width undetermined. Rostrum length 1.34 mm, thickness in front of eye 1.0 mm, short, stout, straight, continuous with head, dorsad, and ventral outlines straight. Scrobes deep, passing beneath near where ventral edge of rostrum joins head. Scape nearly attaining the eye, slightly curved, inserted in apical third, slightly longer than

[1]Entomology, California State College at Long Beach, Biological Sciences Contribution no. 15.

131

funicle; funicle ratio of segments 2.5:1.5:1.5:1.5:1.4:1.4:1.0. Club oval-acuminate, about one-half as long as funicle. Eye strongly transverse, finely granulate. Prothorax length 2.6 mm, thickness (dorso-ventrally) 1.3 mm, densely closely punctured dorsally and laterally; disc convex in outline. Elytra length and width undetermined; humeri prominent; striae laterally conspicuously deeply punctate, punctures round and separated by 1 to 1.5 times their diameter, each with a reclinate setose scale, striae 6 and 7 joined behind humeri; intervals flat, as wide as to 1.5 times wider than striae. All femora strongly clubbed, front length 2.5 mm, width just behind apex 0.6 mm. Front tibiae slender, slightly curved, strigose, nearly as long as the femora, with a strong incurving hook apically. Tarsi as in typical *Cleonus,* but with fourth segment missing, front tarsal segments present about as long as femora.

OTHER MATERIAL: Paratype, same data as holotype, no. B153, a lateral aspect of prothorax, elytra, and the femora of front, middle, and hind legs of right side. Length of preserved parts 9.5 mm, width undetermined, thickness (dorsum of elytra to ventral surface of metasternum) 3.0 mm.

Nearest our present day *Cleonus stratus* Csiki (probably better known as *sparsus* LeConte), but with shorter, straighter, thinner rostrum, straighter scrobes; elytral punctures smaller and the elytral intervals subequal.

Cleonus (Cleonidius) channingensis, n. sp.
(Pl. 20, fig. 4)

HOLOTYPE: Texas, Hartley County, Mustang Draw (Rita Blanca lake deposits). Dorsal aspect, collection no. B248.

Length 7.5 mm, width 2.75 mm. Rostrum length 1.25 mm, width 0.6 mm, nearly as long as pronotum, longer than the head; dorsal outline parallel sided. Scrobes lateral, deep. Antennae inserted in apical fourth, remainder not visible. Head continuous with rostrum, alutaceous. Eyes transverse laterally, coarsely granulated. Prothorax length 1.5 mm, width 2.25 mm. Sides parallel with a rather feeble apical constriction; pronotum closely, coarsely, deeply punctured; base strongly sinuate. Elytra length 5.5 mm, width 2.75 mm, slightly wider and 3.5 times longer than the prothorax. Humeri feeble but present, sides parallel to apical fourth then strongly convergent to apex; striae feebly impressed on disc, deeply on sides, with small, deep, round punctures, separated by more than twice their diameter. Femora feebly clubbed. Tibiae narrow, flattened, nearly as long as femora.

OTHER MATERIAL: Dorsal imprint of B248, bearing number B182.

This species is closest to our present day *C. circumductus* Casey, but differs from that species by its flatter elytral intervals and the punctures of the striae larger and more distantly separated. The sides of the prothorax are more parallel, the pronotum more closely punctured, and the rostrum shorter than in *C. circumductus.*

Present-day forms nearest to the aforementioned species are encountered chiefly in rather arid environments. These forms are frequently encountered in southwestern United States on such plants as *Artemisia tridentata* and *A. nova, Hymenoclea* spp., *Astragalus* spp., and some species of *Ambrosia.* It would seem that we can assume that these fossil forms lived in a similar environment, one very similar to our present Great Basin Desert as outlined by Jaeger (1957).

ACKNOWLEDGMENTS

The author wishes to acknowledge the aid of Dr. William Lumsden of California State College at Long Beach and Mr. Vincent Caccese of the library staff of that institution.

REFERENCES CITED

Jaeger, E. C., 1957, The North American deserts: Stanford, Stanford Univ. Press, 308 p.

Scudder, S. H., 1900, Canadian fossil insects: Ottawa, Canadian Paleontology II Contr., pt. 2

Fishes of the Rita Blanca Lake Deposits

WILLIAM J. KOSTER

University of New Mexico, Albuquerque, New Mexico

INTRODUCTION

Seventy-six specimens of fossil fish from the Rita Blanca lake deposits were submitted for study. Two species, *Fundulus zebrinus,* the southwestern plains killifish, and *Lepomis megalotis,* the longear sunfish, were recognized. These are the first fossil records of these species, and today both inhabit the shallow waters of lakes and streams of the southern High Plains. It is possible that other species are represented among the small, fragmentary individuals of *Lepomis.* Comments on the identification, ecology, and paleogeography are made below.

The specimens had been obtained from a zone ranging from about $T_0 + 200$ to $T_0 + 400$ units near the base of the varve sequence. The fish had apparently been transported to, and buried in, the deeper part of the lake. Their preservation ranges from poor to good, and, although the bones of most specimens are badly crazed or fractured, the pigment melanin is visible in many.

SYSTEMATIC DESCRIPTIONS

Class OSTEICHTHYES
Order ANTHERINIFORMES
Family CYPRINODONTIDAE
Fundulus cf. F. zebrinus
(Jordan and Gilbert)
(Pl. 23, figs. 1, 2, 4)

Sixty-six specimens, about 13 to 55 mm, standard length, are included in the collection. Although some of the specimens are in poor condition and cannot be identified by themselves, there is no reason to believe that more than one species is represented.

That they are members of the family Cyprinodontidae is indicated by the following characters: fins entirely of soft rays; pectoral fin base vertical; caudal fin truncate;

135

teeth present only on premaxillaries, dentaries, and pharyngeals; margin of upper jaw formed entirely by the premaxillaries; scales present on top of head; and anal fin not modified into a gonopodium.

The genus *Fundulus* is indicated by the relatively long, slender, ascending process of the premaxilla; the undivided hypural plate (Miller, 1955b); the five branchiostegal rays; and the simple, conical teeth on the jaws and pharyngeal bones.

Among the Recent species within the Genus *Fundulus,* the specimens are closest to *F. zebrinus.* Indicative characteristics are: the origin of the dorsal fin, slightly in advance of the anal fin; the scale counts in the low forties; the dorsal and anal fins with about 13, with possible extremes of 11 and 15, rays; the comparatively short caudal peduncle, which is about one-fourth the standard length; and, curiously, certain features of pigmentation that have been preserved. Many of the specimens show a black peritoneum, and several show a distinct dark spot on the mid-line just in advance of the dorsal fin. In addition to these somewhat diagnostic color features, pigment also remains on the top of the head, on the scale pockets, and along some of the former blood vessels.

On the basis of modern distribution, *Fundulus kansae* (Garman), which shares most of the above characteristics with *F. zebrinus,* was more to be expected. *F. kansae* is the species presently found in the Canadian Basin, whereas *F. zebrinus* is found natively only in drainages to the south and southwest of the Canadian. The two species are close and may be conspecific (Miller, 1955a). As compared with *F. zebrinus, F. kansae* has smaller eyes and smaller scales. It usually has more than 52 scales in a lateral series. The 13 scale counts made on the fossils are only approximations, but all are closer to 40 than to 50. The eyes can not be accurately measured, but their size seems to be closer to that of *F. zebrinus* of appropriate standard length. The preorbital bone, which is normally used as a basis of comparison with the eye in these species, was in all cases too badly damaged to be of use.

Among the fossil species of *Fundulus,* the Rita Blanca fossils most closely resemble *F. sternbergi* Robertson (1943) (probably = *F. detillai* Hibbard and Dunkle, 1942). *Plancterus* [=*Fundulus*] *kansae*? reported by Stovall and McAnulty (1939) is a species of *Menidia* according to Hubbs (1942). *Fundulus detillai* and *F. sternbergi* are considered close to *F. kansae* (Smith, 1962). These two species, which were described from the same horizon and locality in the Ogallala Formation, Logan County, Kansas, were synonomyzed by Miller (1955a) and Smith (1962). On the other hand, Uyeno and Miller (1963) recognized the two forms pending a re-examination of the types because "the type descriptions contain a number of statements that clearly distinguish the two." The Channing fossils differ from the type description of *F. sternbergi* in having the origin of the dorsal fin anterior to the origin of the anal instead of opposite. They differ from the descriptions of both species in being more slender and in having larger eyes and a different number of branchiostegal rays. *F. detillai* is said to have four and *F. sternbergi* six. Like *F. zebrinus* and *F. kansae,* the Rita Blanca fish have five.

Examination of the type-series of *F. sternbergi* casts doubt on some of these differences and further doubt on the specific distinctness of *F. detillai* and *F. sternbergi. Fundulus detillai* was described by Hibbard and Dunkle (1942) as having both the maximum length of the head and the depth of the body greater than one-third the length of the body, the dorsal fin slightly in advance of the anal fin, and four branchiostegal rays. *F. sternbergi* was described by Robertson (1943) as having the head and depth less than one-third of the body length, the origin of the dorsal fin opposite that of the anal, and six branchiostegal rays. The relative size of the head and depth of the body of *F. detillai* were probably misstated by Hibbard and Dunkle (1942); the type plate and measurements given in the text indicate these parts as being less, rather than more, than one-third of the body length. On the other hand, Robertson states that the origin of the dorsal fin of *F. sternbergi* is directly opposite the origin of the anal. The holotype, however, is twisted, and any measurement of this point is uncertain. In the two para-types, the dorsal is slightly in advance of the anal fin, as it is said to be in *F. detillai*. The number of branchiostegal rays in the holotype of *F. sternbergi* appears to be four, or possibly five; in one of the two paratypes, five, or possibly six. Little remains to separate the two forms.

Although the similarities between the Rita Blanca *Fundulus* and *F. sternbergi* (prob-ably = *F. detillai*) are great, the similarities with *F. zebrinus* are greater.

Assuming the identification of the Rita Blanca *Fundulus* as *F. zebrinus* to be correct, the presence in Blancan times of *F. zebrinus* in an area currently occupied by *F. kansae* suggests a change in the fauna of the Canadian River, in the drainage affinity of the Rita Blanca area, or both. Because *F. kansae* occurs to the north and *F. zebrinus* to the south and southwest, any possibility might be correct. The available evidence is inconclusive.

The suggestion of a change in the drainage pattern comes from Baker (1915). He stated that because the Palo Duro Fork of the Red River arises near the northwestern corner of the Llano Estacado, the suggestion was inevitable that the Red River formerly headed farther west and was later decapitated by the Pecos or Canadian Rivers. *Fundulus* from the Red River Basin in Oklahoma have been identified as *F. kansae* by Hubbs and Ortenburger (1929). However, some specimens of *Fundulus* from Palo Duro Canyon State Park, Texas, have the larger scales and eyes characteristic of *F. zebrinus*; others have the smaller scales characteristic of *F. kansae*. Perhaps this is an admixture brought about by stream piracy.

COLLECTION: University of New Mexico, 2348, 2349, 2350, 2351, 2352, 2353, 2354, 2355, 2356, 2357, 2358, 2359, 2360, 2361, 2362, 2363, 2364, 2365, 2366, 2367, 2368, 2369, 2370, 2371, 2372, 2373, 2374, 2375, 2376, 2377, 2378, 2379, 2380, 2381, 2382, 2383, 2384, 2385, 2386 a and b, 2387, 2388 a–e, 2389, 2390, 2391, 2392, 2393, 2394, 2395, 2396, 2397, 2398, 2399, 2400, 2401, 2402, 2403, 2404, 2405, 2406, 2407, 2408, 2409, 2410; West Texas State Museum, P60-8, P60-10, P60-13.

Order PERCIFORMES
Family CENTRARCHIDAE
Lepomis cf. *L. megalotis* (Rafinesque)
(Pl. 23, figs. 3, 5)

The best preserved centrarchid is West Texas State Museum no. P60-87. The speci-men is split sagitally and is in three pieces. The left side of the head and much of the right side of the head, trunk, and tail are represented. This individual represents *Lepomis megalotis* or an undescribed species close to it.

The genus *Lepomis* of the family Centrarchidae is indicated for this spiny-rayed fish by: the conjoined spiny and soft dorsal fins, the three anal spines, the three predorsal bones, the terminal mouth, the smooth margin to the preopercle, and the deep body.

That this represents *L. megalotis* rather than some other Recent species of *Lepomis* is suggested by: the strongly arched predorsal profile; the toothless palatine area; the large, opercular flap, which is striated, but not especially fimbriated, wider than the apparent diameter of the eye, and distinctly longer than wide; the nearly straight base to the anal fin; the size of the longest anal spine, about half the distance between the insertions of the pelvic and anal fins; the pectoral fin, which appears to be short and with about 13 rays; and by the scales on the breast which are not greatly different from those on the lower sides.

The fossil differs from typical *L. megalotis* in several ways. According to Smith and Bailey (1961), *Lepomis* has a predorsal-bone formula of 0-0-0-1 or 0-0-0-0-2. Three predorsal bones and apparently two spines arising from the first pterygiophore give a formula of 0-0-0-2 for this specimen. Matching spine for spine of the dorsal fin of the fossil with those of a Recent specimen of comparable size, the spines on the fossil appear short, only about two-thirds as high as those on the Recent fish. This difference disappears, however, if spines 2,3,4, and so on, are matched with 1,2,3, and so on, of the Recent fish. This and the unusual predorsal formula suggest that the first spine of the fossil is an anomaly or represents one that has since been lost by the species. The anal fin has 11 instead of the usual 10 rays. An accurate count was not possible, but there appear to be a few more scales in the predorsal series in the fossil. The opercular flap extends about to a vertical from the origin of the pelvic fins or about the fifth or sixth rather than the fourth dorsal spine. Remains of the color pattern indicate much less black on the opercular flap. Instead of covering most of the flap as is usual in *L. megalotis,* the black is largely restricted to a crescent close to the tip. Beyond the crescent is a narrow, pale band.

This appears to be the first fossil record of *L. megalotis.*

COLLECTION: West Texas State Museum no. P60-87.

cf. *Lepomis*

Included here are nine fragmentary specimens. Eight are small, approximately 16 to 50 mm, standard length, relatively deep-bodied, spiny-rayed fish that can not be identified with certainty to *Lepomis* but which appear to be young sunfish. There seem to be 3 spines in the anal fin and 10 in the dorsal. The dorsal fin is undivided. Although several individuals match *L. megalotis* of comparable size fairly well, others compare less well. It is possible that more than one species is present. A fragment of a larger fish, no. 1-365, represented by the caudal fin and part of the caudal peduncle with ctenoid scales is provisionally included here on the basis of aspect.

COLLECTION: University of New Mexico nos. 2411, 2412, 2413, 2414, 2415, 2416, 2417; West Texas State Museum nos. 1-365, 1-368, 1-369.

ECOLOGY

The evidence from the fossil fish is consonant with the concepts that Rita Blanca Lake was saline or alkaline and that in some cases the animal fossils represent death assemblages. Modern representatives of both species are found in relatively saline waters, but are by no means restricted to them. The absence of other, less tolerant, species may represent either negative evidence of saline conditions or simply sampling error. That a catastrophe, rather than old age or post-spawning debility, was the cause of death is suggested because many of the specimens are small, of a size normally associated in modern individuals with a juvenile condition. A catastrophe is further suggested by finding two young *Fundulus* superimposed.

ACKNOWLEDGMENTS

I wish to thank Meryl Walker, Curator, Fort Hays Kansas State College Museum, for the loan of the type series of *Fundulus sternbergi;* Lonnie Peters, Biologist, Texas Parks and Wildlife Department, for fish collected in Palo Duro Canyon; and especially J. T. Hughes, Curator of Paleontology, West Texas State Museum, for the loan of fossil fish from the Rita Blanca collection.

REFERENCES CITED

Baker, C. L., 1915, Geology and underground waters of the Northern Llano Estacado: Texas Univ. Bull., no. 57, 225 p.

Hibbard, C. W., and Dunkle, D. H., 1942, A new species of cyprinidontid fish from the Middle Pliocene of Kansas: Kans. Geol. Survey Bull., v. 41 (Repts. of studies, Pt. 7), p. 270–276

Hubbs, C. L., 1942, An atherinid fish from the Pliocene of Oklahoma: Jour. Paleontology, v. 16, no. 3, p. 399–400

Hubbs, C. L., and Ortenburger, A. I., 1929, Notes on Oklahoma fishes: Okla. Univ. Biol. Survey Pub., v. 1, no. 2, p. 17–43

Miller, R. R., 1955a, An annotated list of the American cyprinodontid fishes of the Genus *Fundulus,* with the description of *Fundulus persimilis* from Yucatan: Mich. Univ. Mus. Zoology Occasional Papers, no. 568, p. 1–26

—— 1955b, A systematic review of the Middle American fishes of the Genus *Profundulus*: Mich. Univ. Mus. Zoology Misc. Pub., no. 92, p. 1–64

Robertson, G. M., 1943, *Fundulus sternbergi,* a Pliocene fish from Kansas: Jour. Paleontology, v. 17, p. 305–307

Smith, C. L., 1962, Some Pliocene fishes from Kansas, Oklahoma, and Nebraska: Copeia, p. 505–520

Smith, C. L., and Bailey, R. M., 1961, Evolution of the dorsal-fin supports of percoid fishes: Mich. Acad. Sci., Arts, and Letters Papers, 1960 mtg., v. 46, p. 345–363

Stovall, J. W., and McAnulty, W. N., 1939, Cyprinodontidae from the Pliocene in Roger Mills County, Oklahoma. Am. Midland Naturalist, v. 22, p. 749–752

Uyeno, Teruya, and Miller, R. R., 1963, Summary of Late Cenozoic freshwater fish records for North America: Mich. Univ. Mus. Zoology Occasional Papers, v. 631, p. 1–34

Part IV. Synthesis

Paleoecology of the Rita Blanca Lake Area

ROGER Y. ANDERSON

University of New Mexico, Albuquerque, New Mexico

DOUGLAS W. KIRKLAND

Mobile Research and Development Corporation, Dallas, Texas

INTRODUCTION

The following account of the paleoecology of the Rita Blanca lake area gathers information presented in earlier sections of this report into a general description of the physical setting of the lake and its associated fauna and flora. It also describes and interprets some of the processes operating within and around the lake, and makes some inferences about the climate of the region.

Many statements of a descriptive nature are made without documentation in this paper, but the above writers have used information that is supported by evidence presented by themselves and by others in the previous sections of the report. The source of information has been given where the conclusions of others have been used in interpretation, and citations have been made where additional information has been used to clarify a conclusion or an interpretation.

SETTING IN TIME AND SPACE

Rita Blanca Lake occupied a deflation basin on what is now the High Plains of Texas during a brief interval of the early Pleistocene. Shortly after its formation, the lake probably became chemically stratified and the seasonal

141

increments of sediments on the lake bottom eventually became preserved as varves. This series of varves occupied only 1,400 years of early Pleistocene time. In the uppermost part of the varved section, the varves thicken by about an order of magnitude before they grade into the nonlaminated sediments above. This suggests a much greater rate of sedimentation for the bulk of the deposit, and the entire history of the lake as a body of water probably represents no more than about 3,000 to 5,000 years. In point of time, the deposition of the Rita Blanca lake beds took place some 1.5 to 3.5 m.y. ago (Evernden and others, 1964).

In understanding the events that took place, the assignment of the Rita Blanca beds to the Blancan provincial age in the mammalian biostratigraphic sequence is more meaningful than the absolute age of the deposit. The Blancan, once assigned to the Pliocene, has in recent years been considered lowermost Pleistocene although there are still disagreements over the position of the Blancan with respect to the boundary. Flint (1965) summarized the conflicting evidence concerning the climate during this interval of time and concluded that there is some indication of climatic fluctuation in both Europe and North America. The physical setting of the Rita Blanca deposit suggests that both the basin and the lake beds were formed during oscillations of more and less available moisture. The caliche cap on the Pliocene Ogallala Group indicates a dry climate with sufficient moisture, however, to leach and accumulate a thick calcium carbonate soil horizon. This interval was followed by general deflation of the Pliocene surface. Deflation is such a common feature of Pleistocene history throughout the High Plains that this mechanism is the most reasonable explanation for the formation of the lake basin. The mere existence of a lake in the deflation basin means a reversal of a climatic trend from less to more available moisture. Hence, the formation and breaching of the caliche and the subsequent filling in of the basin represents a cycle of climatic change over at least several thousands of years.

LAKE ENVIRONS

During its maximum development, Rita Blanca Lake probably had an elliptical shape with a length of about 6 miles and a breadth of about 3.5 miles. The minimum possible depth during formation of the varved sequence was about 30 feet, and the maximum possible depth was somewhat over 125 feet. According to Hutchinson (1957, p. 186), most lakes in relatively easily eroded terrain have a mean depth to maximum depth ratio between 0.33 to 0.50. The development of the shoreline (ratio of the length of the shoreline to the length of the circumference of a circle of area equal to that of the lake) was somewhat greater than a minimum value of 1.05. The trend of elongation of the lake was north-south. Evans and Meade (1945, p. 488) have shown that when water is present in Recent deflation basins of the High Plains there is evidence of contemporaneous increase in the area of the lake at the ends.

A current system probably developed in Rita Blanca Lake which caused wave erosion at the ends of the lake.

The area around the lake was a gently rolling plain of slight relief with the caliche caprock eroded in only a few places by earlier deflation. The drainage basin consisted mainly of sandstone probably mantled by chernozem or brown soil and underlain by a "B" horizon of calcium carbonate. Streams of low competency carried clay and eroded calcium carbonate particles in suspension and calcium carbonate in solution into the lake. The deflation origin of the basin suggests that the sides of the lake were steeper than the general slope of the drainage in the area. The surface of the lake was some unknown distance below the level of the plain, but no more than about 75 feet and probably less. The streams were populated by a species of killifish (*Fundulus* cf. *F. zebrinus*) which is now more common in the plains drainage to south (the present drainage of the Canadian River that has dissected the lake deposits contains *F. kansae*). The presence of the fish implies that the lake basin was open at least during its early stage of development and that the surface of the plains had a reasonably well-integrated drainage pattern, probably trending in a general easterly direction.

A comparison of pollen and leaf floras shows that the vegetation in the area consisted of a mesic riparian or lake-shore element surrounded by a xeric element. Grass pollen are usually under-represented in pollen spectra, and the relative abundance of grass in the fossil pollen record (17 percent) indicates that the drainage area had a moderately well-developed grass cover. Panic grass (*Pancium dichotomiflorum?*), sandbur (*Cenchrus pauciflorus*), and meloid beetles were associated with the grass cover. Sagebrush (*Artemisia*) comprises nearly 50 percent of the pollen flora. Modern pollen rain analogs are not available, but a lake of comparable size surrounded by a pure stand of sagebrush would probably have an even higher percentage of sagebrush pollen, perhaps as high as 80 percent. The frequency of *Artemisia* and grass pollen in the lake sediments suggests mixed sagebrush and grass in the area beyond the margin of the lake. Eolian sand and silt constitute an important fraction of the lacustrine sediments, and the availability of these clastic materials suggests that ground cover by grass was probably incomplete.

No fragments of sagebrush were found in the megafossil record, although two species of weevils (*Cleonus channingensis* and *C. ritablancensis*), the nearest relatives of which are encountered on big sagebrush (*Artemisia tridentata*) were identified. The oaks are the third major element of the xeric flora. The percentage of oak pollen (15 percent) is high for a type of pollen that is usually under-represented in modern spectra. Furthermore, oak leaves, especially *Quercus gambelii,* are the dominant form in the fossil leaf flora. Gambel's oak probably occupied sites near the shore of the lake. A less commonly represented new species, *Q. ritablancensis,* was apparently a shrub that occupied sites removed from the lake, perhaps associated with sagebrush. The specimens assigned to post oak (*Q. stellata*) contain some forms that resemble *Q. lyrata,* a species that prefers moist edaphic conditions, and these oaks may also have occupied sites not far removed from the lake. Several other plant species in the fossil record probably inhabited the area immediately surrounding the riparian community. These include osage orange (*Maclura pomifera*) which prefers flat areas and *Baccharis salicina,* a shrub that is presently found in *Artemisia* and pinyon areas, although normally in moist soil. Other forms, represented only as pollen, such as *Juniperus, Sarcobatus, Ulmus, Juglans, Celtis,* and *Ephedra* may also have been growing within the drainage basin.

The vegetation outside the drainage basin is represented by a number of pollen types that entered the lake through long-distance transport. The genera that most certainly are of this origin include spruce (*Picea*), fir (*Abies*), and probably pine (*Pinus*). Some of the deciduous hardwoods that are rarely represented, and then only by pollen, can probably be included in the same category. These might include maple (*Acer*), birch (*Betula*), alder (*Alnus*), and ash (*Fraxinus*).

A varied riparian flora and insect fauna formed the community around the lake and are represented by leaves or other structures washed into the lake. *Selaginella* and an unknown species of moss occur only as spores. Species known from fragments include the coyote willow (*Salix exigua*), Bebb willow (*Salix bebbiana*), eastern cottonwood (*Populus deltoides*), hawthorn (*Crataegus chrysocarpa*?), smooth indigo bush (*Amorpha laevigata*), western soapberry (*Sapindus drummondii*), *Prunus,* and *Ribes.* Most of the terrestrial insects found as fossils (beetles, wasps, ants, flies, and so forth) probably lived in the riparian community. The fossil mammals associated with the Rita Blanca deposits (horses, camels, elephants) ranged through both the xeric and riparian communities.

The surface water and shallow bottom muds of the lake were host to a number of aquatic insects as well as to fishes, mollusks, and algae. Killifish (*Fundulus* cf. *F. zebrinus*) and sunfish (*Lepomis* cf. *L. megalotis*) occupied the shallow water near shore. Cattails (*Typha*) and ditch grass (*Ruppia maritima*) lined the banks behind the shore. Aquatic vegetation was not abundant, but bur reed (*Sparganium*) grew adjacent to the shore or perhaps in marshy areas in water of reduced salinity. Dragonfly (*Libellulidae*), midge (*Chironomus*) and mosquito (*Culex*) adults were seasonally abundant near the shore and their larvae were common in the shallow-water bottom sediments. The ostracodes *Limnocythere, Candona,* and *Cyprideis* lived on the shallow bottom. The fresher surface water supported populations of the green alga *Pediastrum* and, more abundantly, *Botryococcus.*

TYPE OF LAKE AND ORIGIN OF LAMINATIONS

The association of the fossils and sediments found in Rita Blanca Lake can best be explained if the lake were saline or alkaline and chemically stratified (meromictic). Several lines of fossil evidence suggest a saline, or alkaline condition for the lake. The number of species of fossil aquatic insects in the deposit is much smaller than would normally be expected in a hard-water lake of the temperate zone. J. E. Sublette concluded in his report that the new species *Chironomus kirklandi* had an ecology similar to extant species of *Chironomus* (Halliella) which are all halophitic. He also compiled a chart comparing the Rita Blanca fauna with the fauna found in other modern chemically stratified lakes, and noted a number of species in common. Most of the aquatic insect specimens are benthic forms derived from the littoral and sublittoral zones, but selective transportation and preservation may have resulted in under-representation. If these insects faithfully mirror the near-shore community, some factor, possibly alkalinity, was limiting to many species of aquatic insects.

A similar restriction in the variety of fishes was noted by William J. Koster. The fishes that do occur in the Rita Blanca sediments are also known to tolerate saline or alkaline waters.

William C. Martin noted that the modern association of the aquatic plant species *Ruppia maritima* (ditch grass) found in the Rita Blanca flora is with waters of greater than normal alkalinity or salinity, although *R. maritima* is not necessarily restricted to these environments.

The ostracodes studied by Richard H. Benson provide the best information concerning the probable concentration of dissolved materials in the water. Benson's estimate is a salinity of a 3 to 5 ‰ or alkaline water of a concentration that would produce a similar effect in restricting the types of forms and in determining their ornamentation. These four opinions as to the saline or alkaline associations of the flora and fauna were expressed independently without knowledge of the others' findings.

The sediments contain about 40 percent calcium carbonate, a large portion of which was precipitated within the lake basin. Modern surface waters from the closest measurement stations in the Canadian drainage near Logan and Amarillo, Texas, are high in Ca^{++} and HCO_3^{--} (about 100 ppm Ca^{++}, 300 ppm HCO_3^{--} [Love, 1964]). Jerry Harbour (written commun., 1965) has examined a number of clays from the High Plains area for chlorides and sulfates. Many of the younger samples and samples to the north of the Rita Blanca area contained both of these constituents, but the Rita Blanca samples contained neither. This information, when combined with the mineralogy of the sediments, strongly suggests that the ion concentration was principally as calcium and magnesium and that the lake should properly be classified as a temporary hard-water lake.

Meromixis, a condition of a lake in which some water remains partly or wholly unmixed with the main water mass during intervals of circulation, is generally a normal prerequisite to the preservation of laminae (Bradley, 1929, p. 103; Deevey, 1953, p. 291).

Strøm (1945, p. 1–16) has shown that permanent stratification can be established in lakes by dissolved carbonates. Ruttner (1953, p. 37) points out that:

... a salt content of 1 gram/liter increases the specific gravity by about 0.0008. The difference in density attendant on a change in temperature of from 4° to 5° C amounts to 0.000008. To compensate this difference in density thus requires an increase in salt concentration of only 10 milligrams/liter.

Mermomictic lakes may have an extremely high calcium carbonate content in the monimolimnion. Smith (1941, p. 287) studied a permanently stratified lake in northern Michigan in which the alkalinity, expressed as parts per million of calcium carbonate, ranged from a minimum of 12 at the surface to a maximum of 270 at the bottom. Benson's estimate for Rita Blanca Lake, based on ostracode evidence, is about one order of magnitude greater.

A monimolimnion, once established, is extremely stable and long lived. Hutchinson (1937, p. 116-117) has shown that the loss of salinity by diffusion upward into the overlying water is very slow and that there is often a marked resistance to any tendency for two water bodies of differing salinity to mix. Lake Tokke in southern Norway has a monimolimnion which has apparently been in existence for more than 6,000 years (Strøm, 1955). A chemically stratified lake can be considered as two lakes, one above the other. Wind blowing across such a lake will set only the upper zone or mixolimnion, into motion, while the monimolimnion will contain only slow-moving currents. Terrestrial organisms or organisms that lived in the mixolimnion which were transported into the stagnant monimolimnion would be well preserved because of rapid burial and the lack of scavengers.

Chemical stratification in Rita Blanca Lake may have originated indirectly by climatic fluctuations in the following manner: (1) a small lake originated in the late Pliocene deflation basin during a moist climatic interval; (2) a dry interval followed in which evaporation exceeded influx and calcium carbonate and other salts became concentrated; (3) re-establishment of a wet interval and an influx (probably rapid) of fresh water over the saline water established chemical stratification; (4) decomposition of organic matter in the bottom sediments by anaerobic bacteria yielded carbon dioxide and hydrogen sulfide which increased the acidity and tended to heighten and preserve the high salt concentration. No pyrite was observed in the sediments, but only weathered surface material was available for inspection.

The scarcity of varves in modern, nonglacial lake sediments is largely a result of reworking by benthonic organisms (Lenz, 1921, p. 328; Twenhofel and McKelvey, 1941, p. 847; Deevey, 1953, p. 291; Ruttner, 1953, p. 182; Swain, 1961, p. 519). Larger benthonic organisms often occur in great abundance when environmental conditions are ideal; the profundal zone of some lakes, for example, is reported to contain over 71,000 megascopic organisms per square meter (Eggleton, 1939, p. 130). The finely laminated Rita Blanca sequence shows no evidence of disturbance by organisms.

The fossil fauna and flora represent a transported death assemblage. All the fossils with the exception of the saprolegnian? spores were probably once living outside the profundal zone. An interesting observation in support of this interpretation is that occasionally several dragonfly nymphs were closely associated on the same bedding plane. Clusters of nymphs comprising six or more specimens were noted by Carpenter (1957, p. 116). Competition between dragnofly nymphs precludes close association and suggests that the Rita Blanca occurrence for the most part represents a death assemblage.

The varved sequence was deposited in the deepest part (profundal zone) of Rita Blanca lake in an environment free of strong currents. Sediments of sand dimension in most lakes may hardly be expected to extend more than a few hundred yards from shore (Twenhofel and McKelvey, 1941, p. 838), unless carried by turbidity currents, and there is no evidence for this in the Rita Blanca material. Sand undoubtedly occurred along the shore of Rita Blanca lake, as sand-sized particles occur in caddis fly cases. Caddis fly larvae collect in shallow fresh-water habitats only where an adequate supply of oxygen is present (Pennak, 1953, p. 568), and the several specimens of caddis fly cases in the varves were probably introduced from the littoral zone into deeper water by one of the mechanisms suggested by Moretti (1955).

The ostracodes, although benthonic forms, probably did not live in the profundal zone but were transported into the deeper part of the lake. The paucity of adult forms and the virtual absence of articulated carapaces suggest this interpretation, although Benson, in his report, believes that the mixtures of sizes represents a life assemblage. The presence of abundant *Botryococcus* which is known to tolerate more saline conditions than *Pediastrum* (Cookson, 1953; Evitt, 1963) suggests that even the upper layer of water in the lake may have been somewhat saline.

CHANGES WITH TIME

Seasonal Changes

The saline hypolimnion, nearly void of animal life, magnificently preserved the details of seasonal changes within the lake basin. The principal alternation is that of clay and calcium carbonate, representing the winter and summer seasons. The association of organic matter with clay accentuates the seasonal color difference and makes the laminations easily visible. Many other changes were taking place in harmony with the seasons as follows:

(1) Summer: Decreased acidity in the upper zone and maximum deposition of calcium carbonate (up to 65 percent of the total summer sediment); optimum growth season of ostracode genera *Limnocythere* and *Cyprideis*; accumulation of valves probably reached a maximum after spring waters had cleared; maximum rate of deposition of wind-blown silt; pollen-spore spectrum dominated by *Artemisia*; isotopes C^{13} and O^{18} in carbonate relatively abundant; relatively high rate of illite formation or accumulation.

(2) Fall: reduction in the rate of deposition of calcium carbonate; accumulation of leaves, predominantly *Quercus* and *Salix*; accumulation of plant fragments; rate of silt deposition markedly reduced; accumulation of insects;

accumulation of unidentified ostracode; marked decreased in the rate of sedimentation.

(3) Winter and early spring: possible ice cover on the lake prevented silt deposition; increased acidity and minimum rate of deposition of calcium carbonate (as low as 5 percent of total winter sediment); reduced deposition rate of illite and possibly formation of a small amount of kaolin?; moss spore? dominates the pollen-spore spectrum; sapropel accumulation, partially in the form of a dy-type sediment; isotopes C^{13} and O^{18} in carbonate relatively deficient; growth of saprolegnian spores; optimum growth season of ostracode *Candona* begins.

(4) Spring: increase in calcium carbonate deposition; accumulation of insects begins; marked increase in the rate of deposition; some silt deposition begins; growth season of ostracodes *Limnocythere* and *Cyprideis* begins.

Long-Term Changes

Long-term cycles "recapitulate" the annual cycle in the Rita Blanca varve series. This generalization holds true for practically all the parameters measured or observed in the Rita Blanca deposits, and aids interpretation of the long-term changes that took place. For example, $CaCO_3$, silt, and ostracodes are associated in the summer layer. These three components are also associated in their long-term variations. When $CaCO_3$ deposition was high, silt influx and ostracode production were also high. Similarly, times of increased clay influx, kaolin? formation, organic accumulation, and production of algae or fungal structures were associated with the winter layers and also with each other over the long term.

The similar variation of biota and sediment composition on an annual and long-term basis is illustrated in Figure 34. The only constituent measured that does not seem to follow the seasonal-long-term generalization perfectly is tannin-lignin. The analysis of seasonal layers did not reveal any important differences in tannin-lignin content; the long-term variation is essentially the same as that of organic matter and clay. The light and dark seasonal layers may have a similar tannin-lignin content because the greatest number of large woody plant fragments are associated with the silt in the light layer. Some of the zones of increased tannin-lignin in the varve series are defined by a brown color that begins very abruptly and then dissipates gradually upward with time. The abrupt increase suggests a depositional "accident" or trigger, perhaps a burn in the drainage area or some other event that temporarily increased the amount of tannic acid in the runoff.

The long-term and annual petrologic and biologic changes are related to each other because the same conditions that favor the seasonal growth of ostracodes, algae, or the formation of a particular type of sediment are also changing over intervals of several hundred years. The elevated temperature and increased evaporation of the summer season probably also characterize the long-term climatic changes when the nature of the sediment resembles that of the summer layer. Deevey (1953, p. 291) states, "Calcareous lake deposits

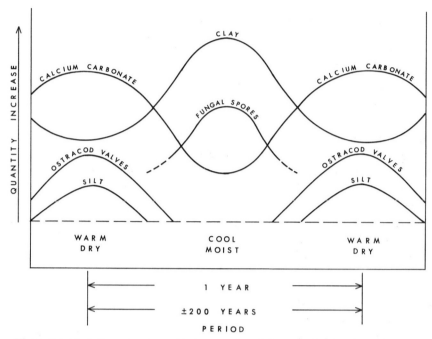

Figure 34. Variation of various biotic and mineral fractions in the Rita Blanca varve series with time.

are likely to be extremely sensitive to climatic variation." He points out (p. 292) that deposition of calcium carbonate is favored by high temperature. The major factor controlling the rate of calcium carbonate deposition is loss of carbon dioxide from the epilimnion during the summer because of increased temperature and photosynthesis. Other factors, such as dilution of the lake water by precipitation in the watershed and changes in atmospheric pressure, may independently affect carbonate deposition, but they are generally of lesser importance.

The rate of clay deposition in a lake depends on several factors; however, the most important are volume of runoff, vegetative cover, and the kind of material available for transport. A grass cover is inferred from the studies of the pollen flora and insects. The pollen profile constructed by Harbour (Fig. 31) suggests that this cover was rather stable during the period of varve formation. The only apparent dynamic factor controlling the amount of clay brought into Rita Blanca lake was the quantity of discharge into the lake, which was largely a function of the amount of precipitation in the drainage basin. Shostakovich (1931, 1936), Journaux (1952, p. 1671), and Granar (1956) have demonstrated a relationship between the thickness of Recent argillaceous nonglacial varves and the amount of precipitation.

Local variations in precipitation within the drainage basin might be a determining factor in clay thickness variation at any one site of deposition. However, quoting Ruttner (1953):

The finest clayey portion, which has a very slow rate of sinking, produces in the lake water a homogeneous turbidity. These clayey particles settle out at approximately the same rate over the entire lake bottom and contribute to the formation of the central plain.

Ruttner's conclusions are supported in Rita Blanca Lake by the varve correlation study which showed very little variation in varve thickness over a distance of several hundred yards. Hence, the fluctuation of the clay component in the varves approximately represents relative fluctuations in annual precipitation.

The graphs of changes in calcium carbonate and clay (Fig. 17; Pl. 7) show the magnitude and length of the long-term oscillations in temperature and precipitation. Anderson and Koopmans (this report) noted that the obvious inverse relationship in long-term variations in the two indices was not maintained for the shorter cycle lengths. In fact, there must be a positive relationship between carbonate and clay deposition over the short term to account for the low coefficient of correlation when all cycle lengths are considered. A possible explanation for the reversal of association with time is found in the source of the carbonate. The long-term variations in carbonate are undoubtedly reflecting long-term changes in evaporation, temperature, and composition of the water in the lake. A lesser fraction of carbonate, however, is apparently derived as a clastic from the drainage basin in association with clay. A season of high runoff that washes in a greater than average volume of clay would also bring in a greater than average amount of calcium carbonate. Hence, the two components would be associated positively on the short-term basis. This effect must be negligible when compared with the gross variations in carbonate production within the lake in order to account for the long-term inverse relationship of the two components. Anderson and Koopmans (this report) found that the inverse effect holds for time intervals greater than about 60–70 years. They also reported the presence of a weak cycle with a period of 22-years in only the carbonate fraction. If the 22-year cycle is real, it suggests that the effects of carbonate precipitation were not completely masked by the influx of carbonate detritus at that scale of change.

In addition to cyclic reversals, the varve series also exhibits a progressive change in the lake environment. The sediment at the base of the varved section is homogeneous, and the annual cycle of clay-carbonate deposition had not yet been established. A seasonal pattern of deposition became firmly established when the lake became meromictic. This transition from non-laminated to laminated clay takes place over an interval of less than a centimeter. Only about six varves are involved in the transition; hence meromixis may have been initiated suddenly. A long period (about 1,150 years) of relative equilibrium prevailed during which the proportions of constituents changed but the average amount for the entire interval remained about the same. During this phase a definite pattern of association of components was established, and they all responded in unison (Pl. 7). The lake had apparently became a balanced ecosystem during this 1,150-year interval.

This period of relative equilibrium was not established at the outset or even for the first 250 years of its chemically stratified history. The correlation between various parameters is low during the first 250 years, but high thereafter. This can be seen in a weak positive relation between clay and $CaCO_3$ in this interval and a negative long-term association for the remainder of the series. The oxygen and carbon isotope ratios are in very close agreement through all of the sequence, except the first 250 years where they are opposite (Pls. 6, 7).

After relative equilibrium was established, the variation in components that did occur was probably the result of climatic changes impressed on the lake and the surrounding area. The changes were cyclic but not particularly periodic, with the average long-term trend in either direction lasting more than 200 years in the first half and about 200 years in the last half of the series. Finally, in the interval above the laminated series which was studied in detail, the varves increased their thickness to as much as a centimeter. The amount of $CaCO_3$ deposited increased very rapidly and the lamination was lost in varied deposition of silt, sand, and clay as the lake became filled in during the shallow water phase of deposition.

BLANCAN CLIMATE

The southern High Plains today is virtually treeless, although cottonwood, willow, elm, walnut, and the woody shrubs mesquite, oak, juniper, hackberry, and *Prunus* are found sparingly in arroyos and along canyons and escarpments. This modern arboreal and shrub vegetation is in marked contrast to the Blancan vegetation, which was dominated by deciduous oak, a variety of other shrubs and trees, and *Artemisia*. Similarly, the fossil pollen spectrum is dominated by *Artemisia*, oak, and Gramineae, whereas the modern spectrum is dominated by chenopod-amaranth type grains, composites other than *Artemisia*, and Gramineae. The difference between Blancan and modern vegetation probably reflects a difference in climate.

Ten of the 13 forms in the fossil leaf flora described by Martin (this report) represent either an aquatic habitat or the riparian community. Several of these species have modern distributions to the east or south of the Rita Blanca deposits in areas of greater moisture than now occurs in the southern High Plains. This distribution does not necessarily mean that the climate resembled that to the southeast, where more moisture is found today, but only that there was sufficient moisture to establish a lake and its associated riparian community.

Harbour concluded from his pollen studies that the climate was cooler and drier than at present. His argument is based on the assumption that the *Artemisia* in the Rita Blanca pollen profile is the big sagebrush of the northern desert shrub areas of the Great Basin and Colorado Plateau. A long winter rest period, the accompanying cold temperatures, and only 10–15 inches of precipitation are factors controlling its modern distribution (Shantz and Zon, 1924). Species of *Artemisia* extant today represent a wide range of elevational, moisture, and soil requirements.

The fact that *Artemisia* must have occurred in a mixed stand in the nearby drainage area in order to account for the high pollen frequencies favors Harbour's interpretation. Today *Artemisia tridentata* is the only species that represents the dominant element in a widely distributed climax community. The other pollen in the deposit such as grass, juniper, and oak are compatable with the moisture and temperature associations of big sagebrush, and the saline nature of the lake also suggests the type of dry local setting that must accompany a stand of big sagebrush. The strongest fossil evidence suggesting that the *Artemisia* pollen is that of big sagebrush and that it represents a northern desert shrub community are the weevils *Cleonus,* identified by E. L. Sleeper. The affinities of these species are with the modern weevils associated with the big sagebrush (*A. tridentata*) in the Great Basin. The other insects in the fauna are either aquatic forms or cannot be identified with the precision necessary to determine their specific climatic associations. The saline affinities of the ostracode species make a comparison with other ostracode faunas in the High Plains difficult; hence they are of less value in climatic comparison than might normally be expected.

The only other species of *Artemisia* that is likely to have contributed pollen in the frequencies observed is the sand sagebrush *A. filifolia* (Loren Potter, oral commun.). This species establishes itself on sand and sand dune areas where there is deep moisture penetration, and occurs on the High Plains today in association with grass and shinnery oak (*Quercus havardii*). It is conceivable that *A. filifolia* established on sand dunes associated with the deflation of the sandstone of the Ogallala could be the species that contributed pollen to the lake sediments. In this case the pollen assemblage could be explained by assuming a much less drastic change in climate. Both of these species of *Artemisia* have spines on their pollen that are reduced or absent, and they cannot be distinguished from one another. Furthermore, the *Artemisia* pollen in the deposit has stronger spine development than either of the two species that are likely to have occurred in the area.

There is some indication that the Pleistocene distribution of big sagebrush was quite different than today, and it may have been one of the forms that changed its distribution pattern in response to general climatic changes associated with glaciation. This interpretation is borne out by the distribution of *Artemisia* pollen in the deep core from Lake San Augustin in New Mexico (Clisby and others, 1959). Prior to the last Pluvial, which introduced a significant frequency of spruce pollen in the upper 230 feet of the lake sediments, the frequency of *Artemisia* increases gradually. *Artemisia* frequencies continue to increase with depth until this pollen comprises an even greater percentage of the pollen spectrum than for Rita Blanca Lake. Local edaphic factors cannot be called upon to explain such a prolonged dominance by *Artemisia,* and big sagebrush (*A. tridentata*) is the only modern analog that seems capable of establishing such a permanent climax community. It is possible that the concept of uniformitarianism is being carried too far in the case of *Artemisia* and problems of speciation may be involved. Until a detailed study of the *Artemisia* problem and *Artemisia* pollen morphology is undertaken, it can only be tentatively concluded that the pollen represents big sagebrush or a species with similar climax associations.

The different moisture conditions suggested by the presence of the lake and the oak leaves and those inferred if big sagebrush were present can be reconciled by assuming that the mean temperature was cooler than at the present time and that under these conditions there would be less transpiration and evaporation and more moisture available to the plants, even with a slightly reduced precipitation. In fact, Rita Blanca Lake may even have had an ice cover during the winter — a condition which would not prevail in the area today. Silt grains which are probably wind blown are essentially restricted to the light-colored summer layer. This phenomenon suggests that ice may have covered the lake during the accumulation of most of the clay and dark layer in the winter.

An ice cover might partially explain the meromictic condition of the lake because Strøm (1945, p. 3) points out that rapid freezing of the surface water of a lake during autumn and late melting of ice in the spring will help preserve chemical stratification. The seasonal distribution of silt grains might also be explained by the occurrence of a blanket of snow over the drainage area. At present the average number of days with snow cover in the Rita Blanca area is about 20, and this does not represent a continuous period. If this figure were increased to 2 or 3 months of the year, the snow cover might effectively shut off the influx of silt grains, and the moisture remaining after the snow melted would tend to prolong the effect.

Although it would be difficult to prove, the textural and compositional associations of the Rita Blanca laminae might be explained best by assuming a shallow alkaline periglacial lake subject to striking seasonal climatic variations. An alternative is that the silt grains were introduced seasonally by flash runoff resulting from summer thunderstorm activity. In the first case, a cooler climate is indicated; in this latter case, a climate more like that of the present time might be possible. The eolian explanation for the deposition of the silt grains appears to be the most plausible, in view of the small size, lack of grading, and uniform lateral distribution of the silt grains, but a fluvial origin cannot be completely excluded from consideration.

Although cooler climate seems indicated, Illinoian pollen spectra from localities about 110 miles to the northeast in Kansas would suggest that the Rita Blanca vegetation does not represent glacial maximum conditions. Kapp's (1965) floras that apparently represent the Illinoian maximum contain much higher frequencies of *Picea* and *Pinus* than does the Rita Blanca flora. However, the difference in age and the unknown association to an existing ice mass makes comparison difficult. The pollen floras that contain the greatest frequency of *Artemisia* and *Juniperus*, and therefore most closely resemble the Rita Blanca flora, are interpreted by Kapp as representing a late Illinoian transition with less moisture and greater climatic extremes than during the glacial maxima. None of Kapp's floras, including interglacial assemblages, contain the very high frequency of *Artemisia* found in the Rita Blanca deposits.

The comparison of Blancan and modern climate in terms of greater or lesser precipitation and higher or lower temperatures is of limited usefulness in understanding the nature of the climatic regime. The departure in temperature and moisture from the modern situation reflects fundamental changes in the movement of air masses during the Pleistocene and the nature of these movements is important to our understanding of the climate.

A type of evidence that is independent of floral and faunal interpretation is available in data collected on a time-series basis from the varved sediments and provides part of the solution to this problem. Long-term climatic fluctuations left their impress on the 1,400-year varve series in the form of major lithologic cycles. Variations in the clay fraction with time represent rainfall and runoff, whereas carbonate fluctuations reflected long-term changes in evaporation and temperature. The inverse association of these two dominant components with time means that there were protracted oscillations on the order of several hundred years of warm-dry and cool-moist climate. The following summary, derived from the petrographic studies of the varves, illustrates the full effect of these extremes of climate on the lake sediments.

(1) Probable climate warm and dry: reduced acidity and maximum rate of calcium carbonate deposition; maximum rate of accumulation of ostracode carapaces; maximum rate of deposition of wind-blown silt; minimum rate of accumulation of organic matter both from production within the lake and from runoff; relatively low rate of illite deposition, hence low influx of runoff from the drainage.

(2) Probable climate cool and moist: increased acidity and minimum rate of calcium carbonate deposition; minimum rate of accumulation of ostracode carapaces; growth of fungal spores common; relatively high rate of deposition of organic matter, including material derived from the drainage through runoff; maximum rate of deposition of allocthonous illite and production of kaolin? within the lake; minimum rate of deposition of silt.

A comparison of this summary of long-term climatically induced oscillations and the seasonal variation summary previously given shows a remarkable similarity of associated annual and long-term events. Extrapolation from seasonal to long-term interpretation of the significance of individual components leads to the deduction that because the long-term changes indicate a cool-moist climate alternating with warm-dry climate, their seasonal analog would indicate warm-dry summers and cool-moist winters. This is not circular reasoning, because the same interpretation of long-term changes would be obtained without using the seasonal analogy. The two types of extrapolation by analogy merely reinforce each other, as they should if the correct interpretation has been made.

The present climatic regime in the Texas Panhandle is far different than the one interpreted from the petrographic changes in the Rita Blanca varve series. Moist winters and dry summers do not occur in the area. Instead, about 80 percent of the precipitation arrives during the warmest 6 months of the year (April–September; Dorroh, 1946), and this is tropical maritime moisture from the Gulf and the Atlantic. Winter-wet and summer-dry climate is only found to the northwest in areas under the influence of Pacific polar maritime air masses.

The long-term oscillation in the Rita Blanca area, as determined by the inverse relationship of precipitation of calcium carbonate and influx of clay, was from cool-moist to warm-dry climate. The greatly increased rates of silt influx during the long dry periods suggests that it was a loss of moisture and perhaps a reduction of the grass cover that made more silt available for transport. One could assume that silt was introduced during prolonged warm intervals by fluvial processes as a result of increased thunderstorm activity. These same processes, however, would also introduce increased amounts of clay in association with the silt. The opposite is actually the case, and it is difficult to avoid the conclusion that a cool-moist and warm-dry climatic regime existed in the area and that the precipitation arrived mainly during the cool season.

One cannot say for certain what changes in sediment composition would be produced by long-term oscillations in the climate of the Texas Panhandle today. Because more than half of the moisture comes from tropical maritime air masses, one might expect oscillations of warmer and wetter conditions with cooler and drier conditions. A complex model could be used to explain the observed association of the carbonate, silt, and clay components under the present climatic regime, but this model could not agree with the simple generalization that seasonal and long-term events parallel each other. Although the simplest explanation is not always correct, in this case it explains most of the observed phenomena.

The floral evidence suggests cooler and perhaps drier conditions for the Rita Blanca occurrence than now prevail in the same area. If the *Artemisia* in the pollen record is big sagebrush or is from a form with similar temperature and moisture requirements, then the petrographic and biologic evidence would be in complete agreement and the climate of the Texas Panhandle during at least part of the Blancan would be similar to the climate of the Great Basin today.

In spite of the fact that a great deal is now known about Rita Blanca Lake, it is difficult to make a dogmatic statement about the climate. The writers feel, however, that the type of lake, the details of petrography, and the associations of the flora and fauna can be explained best by assuming conditions that would result from a shift of the Pacific polar maritime air mass in a general southerly and southeasterly direction. These conditions would include lowered annual temperature, dry summers, and perhaps less precipitation, but with most of it arriving in the cool season.

REFERENCES CITED

Bradley, W. H., 1929, The varves and climate of the Green River Epoch: U.S. Geol. Survey Prof. Paper 154, p. 87–110

Carpenter, F. M., 1957, A Pliocene insect deposit in Texas: Psyche, v. 64, no. 3, p. 116

Clisby, K. H., Foreman, Fred, and Sears, P. B., 1959, Plio-Pleistocene sediments and climates of the San Augustin Plains, New Mexico: N. Mex. Geol. Soc. 10th Field Conf. Guidebook, p. 117–120

Cookson, I. C., 1953, Records of the occurrence of *Botryoccoccus braunii, Pediastrum,* and the Hystrichosphaeridae in Cainozoic deposits of Australia: Melbourne Nat. Mem., v. 18, p. 107–123

Deevey, E. S., Jr., 1953, Paleolimnology and climate, *in* Shapley, Harlow, *Editor, Climatic change, evidence, causes, and effects:* Cambridge, Harvard Univ. Press, 318 p.

Dorroh, J. H., Jr., 1946, Certain hydrological and climatic characteristics of the Southwest: N. Mex. Univ. Pub. in Eng., no. 1, 64 p.

Eggleton, F. E., 1939, Role of the bottom fauna in the productivity of lakes, *in* Moulton, F. R., *Editor,* Problems of lake biology: Am. Assoc. Adv. Sci. Pub. 10, 142 p.

Evans, G. L., and Meade, G. E., 1945, Quaternary of the Texas High Plains: Univ. Texas Pub. 4401, p. 485–507

Evernden, J. E., Savage, D. E., Curtis, G. H., and James, G. T., 1964, Potassium-argon dates and the Cenozoic mammalian chronology of North America: Am. Jour. Sci., v. 262, no. 2, p. 145–198

Evitt, W. R., 1963, Occurrence of freshwater alga *Pediastrum* in Cretaceous marine sediments: Am. Jour. Sci., v. 261, p. 890–893

Flint, R. F., 1965, the Pliocene-Pleistocene boundary, *in* Wright, H. E., Jr., and Frey, D. G., *Editors,* International studies on the Quaternary: Geol. Soc. America Spec. Paper 84, p. 497–533

Granar, L., 1956, Dating of recent fluvial sediments from the estuary of the Angerman River (the period 1850–1950 A.D.): Geol. Fören. Stockholm Förh., v. 78, p. 654–658

Hutchinson, G. E., 1937, A contribution to the limnology of arid regions: Conn. Acad. Arts and Sci., v. 33, p. 116–127

―― 1957, A treatise on limnology: New York, John Wiley & Sons, Inc., 1015 p.

Journaux, Andrè, 1952, Depot actuel de varves lacustres en Normandie: Acad. sci. [Paris] Comptes rendus, v. 235, no. 25, p. 1669–1672

Kapp, R. O., 1965, Illinoian and Sangamon vegetation in southwestern Kansas and adjacent Oklahoma: Mich. Univ. Mus. Paleontology Contr., v. 19, no. 14, p. 167–225

Lenz, Fr., 1921, Schlammschichtung in Binnenseen: Naturwiss. Wochenschr., v. 18, p. 327–329

Love, S. K., 1964, Quality of surface water in the United States, 1962: U.S. Geol. Survey Water-Supply Paper 1944, 645 p.

Moretti, G., 1955, Sulla presenza dei foderi dei Tricotteri e dei Ditteri Tanitarsi sui fondi del Lago Maggiore: Ist. Ital. Idrobial. Mem., supp. 8, p. 205–219

Pennak, R. W., 1953, Fresh-water invertebrates of the United States: New York, Ronald Press, 796 p.

Ruttner, Franz, 1953, Fundamentals of limnology: Canada, Univ. Toronto Press, 242 p.

Shantz, H. L., and Zon, Raphael, 1924, The natural vegetation of the United States, *in* Baker, O. E., 1936, Atlas of American Agriculture: Washington, U.S. Govt. Printing Office, 29 p.

Shostakovich, V. B., 1931, Die Bedeutung der Untersuchung der Bodenablagerungen der Seen für einige Fragen der Geophysik: Internat. Vervand Theoretical Angew. Limnology Verh. Stuttgart, v. 5, p. 307–317

—— 1936, Geschictete Bodenablagerungen der Seen als Klima-Ann.: Meterologische Zeitschrift, v. 53, p. 176–182

Smith, L. L., 1941, A limnological investigation of a permanently stratified lake in the Huron Mountains region of northern Michigan: Mich. Acad. Sci. Arts and Letters, v. 26, p. 281–296

Strøm, K. M., 1945, Lakes with stagnant deeps: Skrifter Norske Vidensk.-Akad., no. 7, p. 1–16

—— 1955, Waters and sediments in the deep of lakes: Ist. Ital. Idriobiol. Mem., supp. 8, p. 345–356

Swain, F. M., 1961, Limnology and amino-acid content of some lake deposits in Minnesota, Montana, Nevada, and Louisiana: Geol. Soc. America Bull., v. 72, no. 4, p. 519–545

Twenhofel, W. H., and McKelvey, V. E., 1941, Sediments of fresh-water lakes: Am. Assoc. Petroleum Geologists Bull., v. 25, no. 5, p. 826–849

Plates

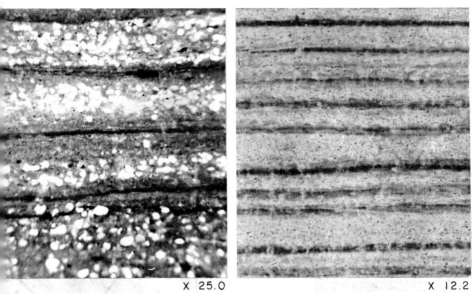

X 25.0

X 12.2

Figure 1. Photomicrograph of thin section of rves from a carbonate-rich clay section

Figure 2. Photomicrograph of polished section of varves from a carbonate-rich clay section

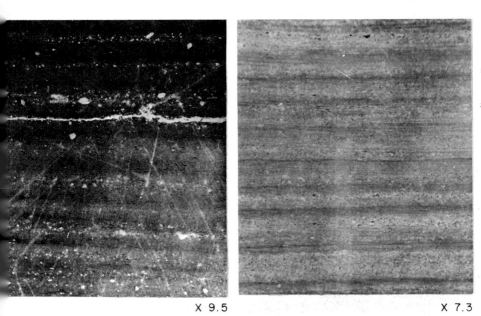

X 9.5

X 7.3

Figure 3. Photomicrograph of thin section of ves from a carbonate-poor clay section

Figure 4. Photomicrograph of a polished section of varves from a carbonate-poor clay section

PHOTOMICROGRAPHS OF RITA BLANCA VARVE SECTIONS

DERSON AND KIRKLAND, PLATE 1
ilogical Society of America Memoir 113

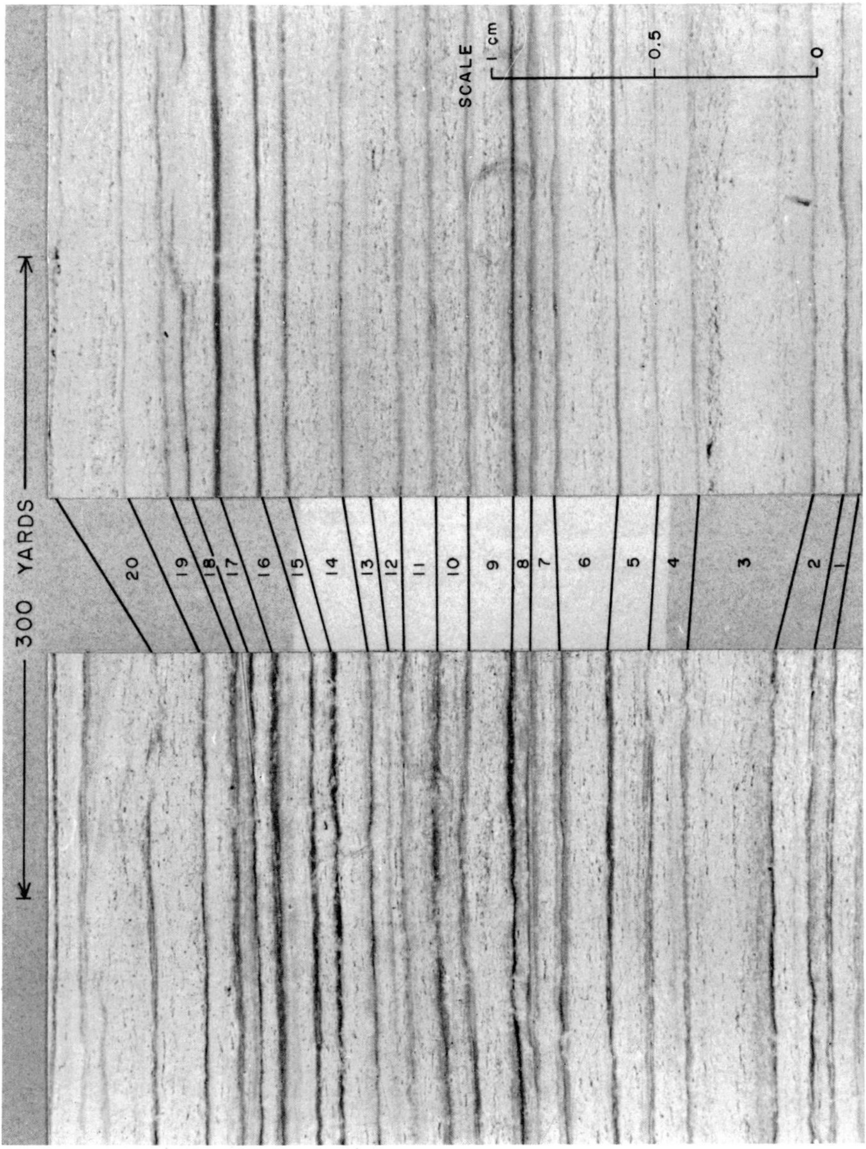

CORRELATION OF VARVES BETWEEN LOCALITIES A AND B

300 YARDS

SCALE
1 cm
0.5
0

ANDERSON AND KIRKLAND, PLATE 2
Geological Society of America Memoir 113

PHOTOMICROGRAPH OF UPPER BEDDING PLANE OF
A LIGHT-COLORED LAMINAE COVERED WITH
A DENSE MAT OF PLANT FRAGMENTS (x@2)

OUTCROP OF VARVED RITA BLANCA LAKE DEPOSITS

Photograph shows long-term alternations of light carbonate-rich and dark carbonate-poor zones.

PLATE 8. RITA BLANCA POLLEN AND SPORES

Figure   Page

1. *Pinus* sp. 86
   Longitudinal view, × 840 (U.N.M. Geol. Dept. slide no. A-23,
   coordinates 113.5 × 28.0 [Leitz Ortholux])
2. *Juniperus* sp. 87
   × 1040 (slide no. A-21, coordinates 29.4 × 126.3)
3. *Quercus* sp. 86
   Equatorial view, × 980 (slide no. A-22, coordinates 25.9 × 109.3)
4. *Quercus* sp. 86
   Polar view, × 1040 (slide no. A-21, coordinates 43.6 × 112.7)
5. Chenopodiacea or Amaranthaceae. 87
   × 1040 (slide no. A-19, coordinates 40.3 × 115.6)
6. *Ephedra* sp. 87
   × 1040 (slide no. A-21, coordinates 33.2 × 126.2)
7. Compositae, subfamily Tubuliflorae. 86
   × 1040 (slide no. A-21, coordinates 30.2 × 119.3)
8. Gramineae. 86
   × 1040 (slide no. A-23, coordinates 40.6 × 111.0)
9. Musci?. 78
   × 1040, deep focus
10. Musci?. 78
    × 1040, high focus

RITA BLANCA POLLEN AND SPORES

RITA BLANCA POLLEN, ALGA, AND OAK LEAVES

ANDERSON AND KIRKLAND, PLATE 9
Geological Society of America Memoir 113

PLATE 9. RITA BLANCA POLLEN, ALGA, AND OAK LEAVES

Figure   Page

1. *Artemisia* sp. 86
   Polar view, × 1040 (slide no. A-21, coordinates 44.8 × 119.1)

2. *Artemisia* sp. 86
   Equatorial view, × 1040 (slide no. A-19, coordinates 27.4 × 118.3)

3. *Botryococcus* sp. 85
   × 520

4. *Quercus gambelii* Nutt. 97
   × 1.0

5. *Q. gambelii* Nutt. 97
   × 1.2

6. *Q. stellata* Wangenheim. 98
   × 0.6

7. *Q. stellata* Wangenheim. 98
   × 1.0

8. *Q. ritablancensis* Tucker n. sp. 98
   × 0.8

PLATE 10. RITA BLANCA LEAVES, INFLORESCENCES, AND STEMS

Figure   Page

1. *Quercus ritablancensis* Tucker n. sp. 98
   × 1.1
2. *Sparganium* sp. 101
   × 2.2
3. *Ruppia maritima* L. 102
   × 1.9
4. *Panicum dichotomiflorum?* Michx. 102
   × 0.6
5. *Cenchrus pauciflorus* Benth. 102
   × 3.0
6. *Salix* cf. *S. exigua* Nutt. 103
   × 1.0
7. *S.* cf. *S. exigua* Nutt. 103
   × 1.4
8. *S.* cf. *S. exigua* Nutt. 103
   × 1.6

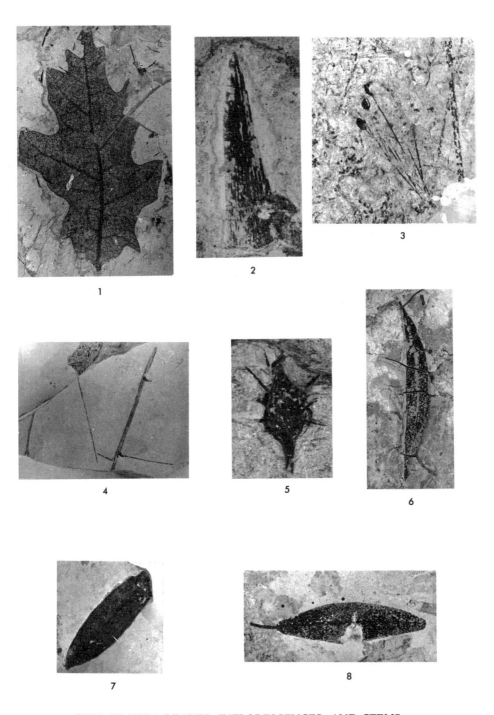

RITA BLANCA LEAVES, INFLORESCENCES, AND STEMS

ANDERSON AND KIRKLAND, PLATE 10
Geological Society of America Memoir 113

RITA BLANCA LEAVES AND ACHENE

PLATE 11. RITA BLANCA LEAVES AND ACHENE

Figure   Page

1. *Salix* cf. *S. exigua* Nutt. 103
   × 1.6
2. *S. bebbiana*? Sarg. 103
   × 1.0
3. *Populus deltoides*? Marsh. 103
   × 1.0
4. *P. deltoides* Marsh. 103
   × 1.1
5. *Maclura pomifera* (Raf.) Schneid. 104
   × 1.0
6. *Crataegus chrysocarpa*? Ashe. 104
   × 1.2
7. *Amorpha laevigata* (Nutt.) Torr. and Gray. 104
   × 1.6
8. *Baccharis salicina* Torr. and Gray, achene. 105
   × 11.1
9. *Amorpha* cf. *A. laevigata* (Nutt.) Torr. and Gray. 104
   × 2.7
10. *Sapindus drummondii*? Hook. and Arn. 104
    × 1.2

PLATE 12. RITA BLANCA ODONATA

Figure   Page

1–3. Naiads of Libellulidae (Odonata), (det. M. J. Westfall). 118
     (1) $\times$ 1.8, (2) $\times$ 3.3, (3) $\times$ .8

  4. Naiads of ?Coenagrionidae (Odonata). 118
     $\times$ 3.9

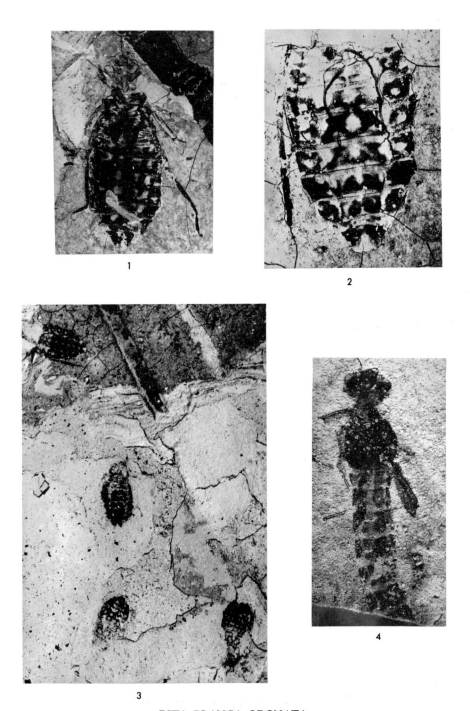

RITA BLANCA ODONATA

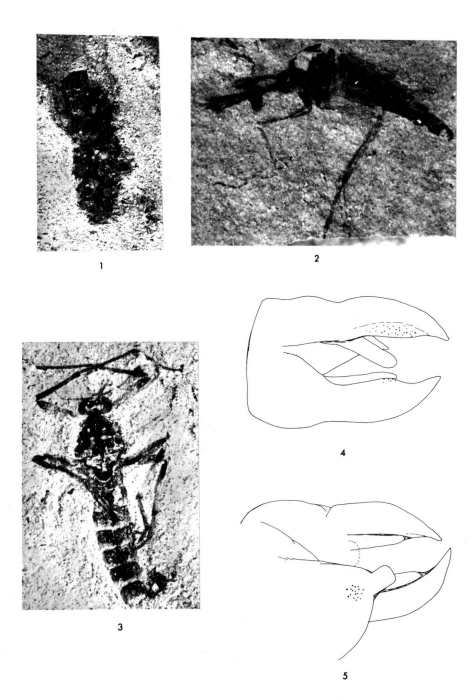

RITA BLANCA TRICHOPTERA AND DIPTERA

PLATE 13. RITA BLANCA TRICHOPTERA AND DIPTERA

Figure   Page

1. Larval case of ?Mollanidae (Trichoptera) (det. H.H. Ross). 118
   × 5.2
2. *Culex* sp., adult male (det. Alan Stone). .:...............................118
   × 7.8
3. *Chironomus* (*Chironomus*) *kirklandi* Sublette n. sp. 119
   (Chironomidae, Diptera) adult male, Paratype. × 9.4
4. *Chironomus* (*Chironomus*) *kirklandi* Sublette n. sp. 119
   Holotype, male genitalia, ventral view.
5. *Chironomus* (*Chironomus*) *kirklandi* Sublette n. sp. 119
   Paratype, male genitalia, dorsal view.

PLATE 14. RITA BLANCA DIPTERA (CHIRONOMIDAE)

Figure   Page

1. *Chironomus (Chironomus) kirklandi* Sublette n. sp. 119
   Allotype, female (lower left) and paratype male (upper right). × 6.0

2, 3. *Chironomus (Chironomus) kirklandi* Sublette n. sp. 119
   Paratype, male. (2) × 7.4, (3) × 6.9

4. *Chironomus (Chironomus) kirklandi* Sublette n. sp. 119
   Pupae. × 5.8

5. *Chironomus (Chironomus) kirklandi* Sublette n. sp. 119
   Labial plate of larva.

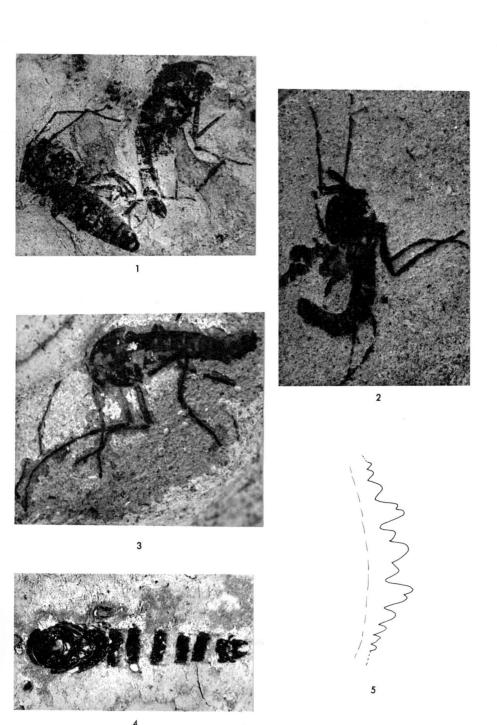

RITA BLANCA DIPTERA (CHIRONOMIDAE)

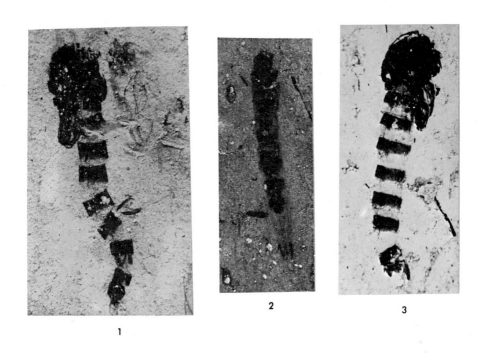

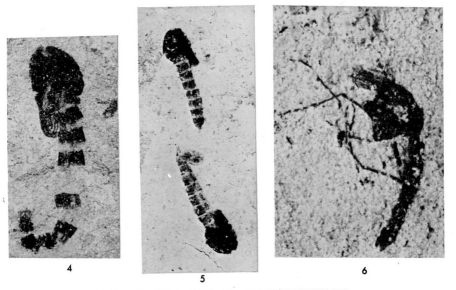

RITA BLANCA DIPTERA (CHIRONOMIDAE)

PLATE 15. RITA BLANCA DIPTERA (CHIRONOMIDAE)

Figure   Page

1–4. *Chironomus* (*Chironomus*) *kirklandi* Sublette n. sp. 119
Pupae, some showing complete ecdysis
(1) × 5.0, (2) × 5.3, (3) × 6.9, (4) × 5.8

5. Sp., ?Orthocladiinae (Chironomidae, Diptera) 120
Pupae. × 6.2

6. Sp., ?Orthocladiinae. 120
Adult male, genitalia details obscure. × 12.6

PLATE 16. RITA BLANCA DIPTERA, HEMIPTERA, HOMOPTERA, AND COLEOPTERA

Figure   Page

1, 2. Sp., ?Tanypodinae (Chironomidae, Diptera) 120
Adult, male. (1) × 10.4, (2) × 9.8

3. Sp., Tingidae (Hemiptera) 124
× 7.0

4, 6. *Nysius*? (Lygaeidae, Hemiptera) 124
(4) × 5.9, (6) × 7.5

5. Sp., Lygaeidae or Corizidae, possibly Coreidae (Hemiptera) 124
× 6.4

7. Sp., cf. Deltocephalinae (Cicadellidae, Homoptera) 125
× 5.9

8. Sp., Aleocharinae? (Staphylinidae, Coleoptera) 126
× 7.3

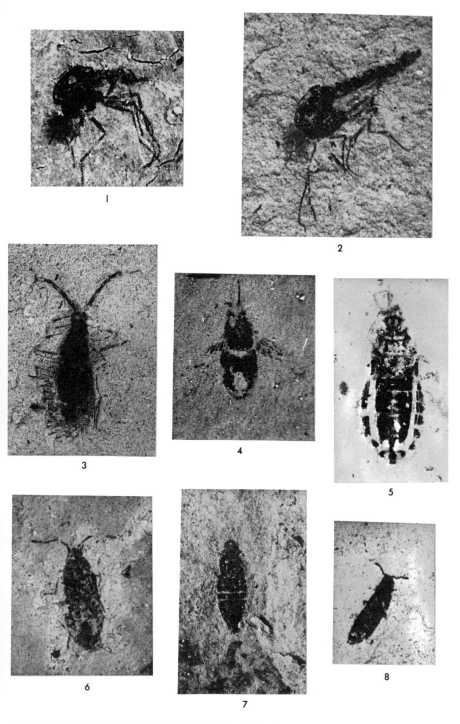

RITA BLANCA DIPTERA, HEMIPTERA, HOMOPTERA, AND COLEOPTERA

ANDERSON AND KIRKLAND, PLATE 16
Geological Society of America Memoir 113

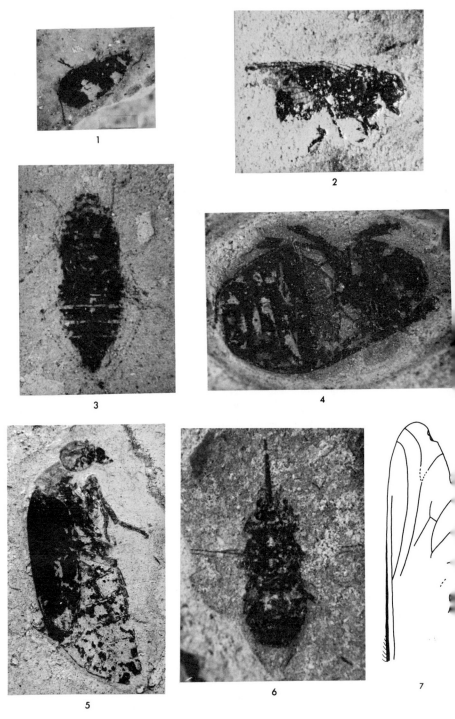

RITA BLANCA COLEOPTERA, DIPTERA, AND HOMOPTERA

ANDERSON AND KIRKLAND, PLATE 17
Geological Society of America Memoir 113

PLATE 17. RITA BLANCA COLEOPTERA, DIPTERA, AND HOMOPTERA

Figure   Page

1. Sp., cf. *Selenophorus* (Carabidae, Coleoptera) 125
   × 4.1
2. Sp. Series Schizophora (Diptera) 127
   × 7.6
3. Sp., Cicadellidae (Homoptera) 125
   × 7.4
4. Sp., cf. *Diplotaxis* (Scarabaeidae, Coleoptera) 126
   × 5.9
5. *Lytta* sp. (Meloidae, Coleoptera) 126
   × 4.6
6. Sp., Bombyliidae (Diptera) 127
   × 7.4
7. Sp., Bombyliidae (Diptera) 127
   Wing venation. × 9.6

PLATE 18. RITA BLANCA DIPTERA AND HYMENOPTERA

Figure   Page

1. Sp., cf. *Syrphus* (Syrphidae, Diptera) 127
   × 6.1
2. Sp., cf. *Syrphus* (Syrphidae, Diptera) 127
   Wing venation. × 9.6
3. Sp., Section Calyptratae (Diptera) 127
   × 6.2
4. Sp., Ichneumonidae (Hymenoptera) 128
   Wing venation. × 9.6
5. Sp., Ichneumonidae (Hymenoptera) 128
   Wing venation. × 9.6
6. Sp., Ichneumonidae (Hymenoptera) 128
   × 5.9
7. Sp., ?Braconidae (Hymenoptera) 128
   × 7.0

RITA BLANCA DIPTERA AND HYMENOPTERA

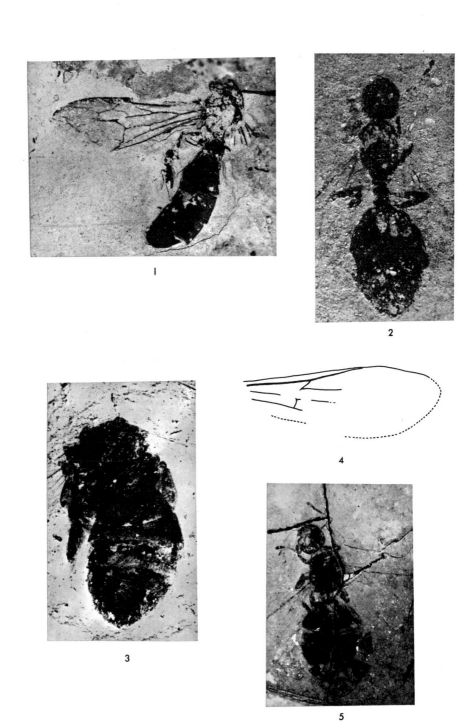

RITA BLANCA HYMENOPTERA

PLATE 19. RITA BLANCA HYMENOPTERA

Figure   Page

1. Sp., Dorylinae–Ecitonini or Cheliomyrmicini (Formicidae, Hymenoptera)..... 128
    × 3.8
2. Sp., Myrmicinae (Hymenoptera) 128
    × 6.1
3. Sp., Apoidea (Hymenoptera) 129
    × 4.3
4. Sp., Pompilidae (Hymenoptera) 129
    Wing venation. × 9.6
5. Sp., Formicinae, sp. (Hymenoptera) 128
    × 4.1

PLATE 20. RITA BLANCA HYMENOPTERA AND COLEOPTERA

Figure   Page
1. Sp., Pompilidae (Hymenoptera) 129
   × 5.1
2. Sp., (Hymenoptera) 129
   × 11.3
3. Leg. Diptera, Hymenoptera, possibly Coleoptera 130
   × 5.2
4. *Cleonus (Cleonidius) channingensis* Sleeper n. sp. 132
   × 6.2
5. *Cleonus (Cleonidius) ritablancaensis* Sleeper n. sp. 131
   × 5.8

1

2

3

4

5

RITA BLANCA HYMENOPTERA AND COLEOPTERA

RITA BLANCA OSTRACODES

PLATE 21. RITA BLANCA OSTRACODES

Figure   Page

1. *Limnocythere* sp. 108
   Right valve of female. × 70 (USNM 649492)
2. *Limnocythere* sp. 108
   Left valve of male. × 70 (USNM 649491)
3. *Candona* sp. 109
   Right valve of immature instar. × 70 (USNAM 649498)
4. *Cyprideis* sp. 109
   Left valve of immature instar. × 70 (USNM 649497)
5. *Candona* sp. 109
   Left valve of male, crushed specimen. No specimens of *Limnocythere* were
   found on the bedding plane where this specimen occurred. × 30
   (USNM 649499)
6–8. *Limnocythere* sp. 108
   Bedding plane showing concentration of poorly preserved immature
   specimens of *Limnocythere* with a very rare fragment of a candonid
   valve (Fig. 7, arrow). × 30 (USNM 649500)

PLATE 22. RITA BLANCA OSTRACODES

Figure   Page
 1. *Limnocythere* sp. 108
    Dorsal view of right valve of a female. × 80
 2. *Limnocythere* sp. 108
    Lateral view of right valve of female, with small hole in anterodorsal region.
    × 80
 3. *Limnocythere* 108
    Lateral view of left valve of male. × (USNM 649493–4)
 4. *Cyprideis* sp. 109
    Dorsal view of left valve adult specimen. × 80
 5. *Cyprideis* 109
    Interior view of left valve of adult specimen showing the cyprideisid hinge
    and muscle-scar pattern. × 80
 6. *Cyprideis* 109
    Lateral view of the exterior of the right valve of possible adult male, showing
    the fine punctate surface and the shallow dorsolateral sulcus. × 80
    (USNM 649495–6)

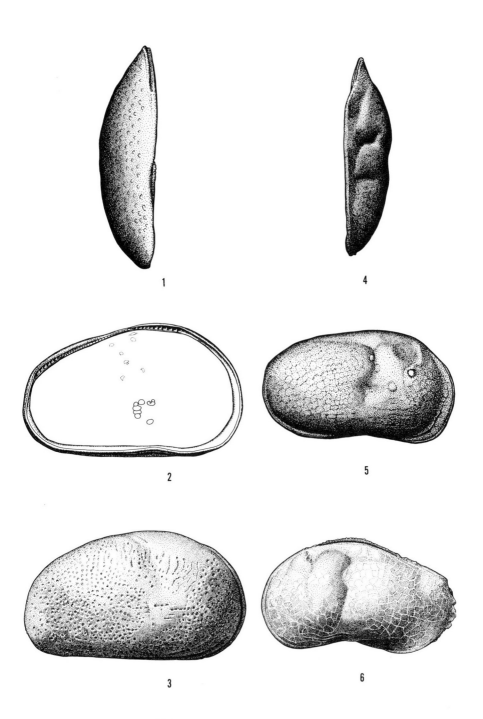

RITA BLANCA OSTRACODES

ANDERSON AND KIRKLAND, PLATE 22
Geological Society of America Memoir 113

1

2

3

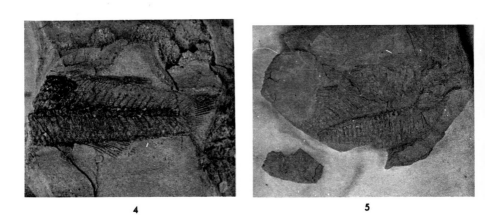

4

5

RITA BLANCA FISH

ANDERSON AND KIRKLAND, PLATE 23
Geological Society of America Memoir 113

Plate 23. RITA BLANCA FISH

Figure   Page

1, 2, 4. *Fundulus* cf. *F. zebrinus* 135
    (1) × 1.6, (2) × 3.8, (4) × 2.2

3, 5. *Lepomis* cf. *L. megalotis* 137
    × 0.5

PLATE 24. RITA BLANCA OSTRACODES AND PELECYPODS

Figure   Page

1. Unknown ostracode, Ilyocypridae? 30, 79
   Bedding plane (base of dark-colored layer), showing the distribution of
   unknown ostracode (family Ilyocypridae?). × 5.1

2. *Pisidium*? sp. 79
   × 6.6

3. Ilyocypridae? and unknown form 30, 79
   × 4.9

4. *Pisidium*? sp. 79
   × 6.6

1

2

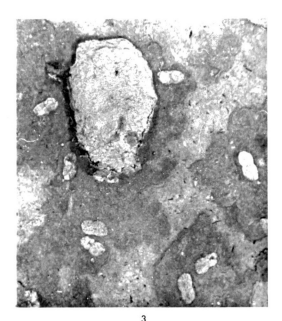

3

4

RITA BLANCA OSTRACODES AND PELECYPODS

APPENDIX I

Summary of Analyses of Parameters Determined in the Rita Blanca Varve Series on a 5-Year or 20-Year Sampling Interval

Time interval T_0+x (in years)	Thickness (in mm)	Color index	Percent CaCO$_3$	Percent MgCO$_3$	Percent Kjeldahl nitrogen	Percent tannic acid	d C^{13}	d O^{18}
0–20	20.2*	84	22†	...	.0133	.030	−2.88	−7.13
21–40	24.3*	77	26†	...	.0161	.020	−3.56	−6.62
41–60	19.0	68	24†	...	.0095	.029	−3.34	−6.40
61–80	18.4	48	34†	...	.0100	.024	−3.97	−5.98
81–100	18.8	35	30†	...	.0054	.028	−4.66	−6.51
101–120	17.3	58	20†	...	.0067	.019	−4.95	−6.92
121–140	22.4	42	30†	...	.0030	.024	−5.30	−5.87
141–145	5.8	12	24†	...	.0057	.023	..	..
151–155	3.5	20	34†	...	.0052	.014	−5.04	−5.76
161–165	2.8	15	30†	...	.0086	.030	−4.29	−5.13
171–175	4.3	33	28†	...	.0061	.029	−4.05	−5.44
181–185	4.2	41	30†	...	.0053	.033	−3.47	−3.72
191–195	3.5	13	34†	...	.0045	.027	−3.33	−4.44
201–205	2.9	25	34†	...	.0056	.031	−4.66	−5.97
211–215	3.4	70	21	4	.0090	.046	−3.25	−3.54
221–225	4.7	83	22	2	.0060	.079	−2.96	−4.58
231–235	4.0	104	18	3	.0065	.186	−3.45	−3.28
241–245	3.5	107	9	3	.0094	.124	−4.86	−7.85
251–255	4.8	112	11	3	.0092	.093	−4.75	−5.38
261–265	5.8	113	11	2	.0098	.087	−4.13	−5.00
271–275	7.0	106	14	2	.0114	.032	−3.82	−3.42
281–285	4.8	91	13	2	.0108	.026	−4.37	−5.54
291–295	5.0	34	29	2	.0040	.026	−3.96	−3.76
301–305	4.4	31	31	2	.0065	.023	−3.69	−2.82
311–315	3.2	44	36	3	.0057	.039	−3.26	−2.71
321–325	2.2	30	34	3	.0089	.020	−3.21	−2.74
331–335	4.6	7	29	3	.0130	.034	−4.26	−3.80
341–345	1.8	73	30	1	.0080	.035	−4.04	−2.90

Time interval T_0+x (in years)	Thickness (in mm)	Color index	Percent CaCO₃	Percent MgCO₃	Percent Kjeldahl nitrogen	Percent tannic acid	d C¹³	d O¹⁸
351–355	2.8	40	36	2	.0065	.043	−4.33	−4.70
361–365	5.2	24	27	3	.0091	.057	−4.26	−4.29
371–375	6.0	22	41	3	.0067	.020	−3.72	−2.85
381–385	4.8	52	34	4	.0064	.037	−4.24	−3.14
391–395	3.9	43	45	4	.0050	.037	−4.55	−3.16
401–405	5.1	9	53	3	.0047	.025	−5.17	−5.55
411–415	4.0	49	30	2	.0057	.032	−4.72	−3.68
421–425	5.1	6	50	2	.0057	.032	−4.16	−3.82
431–435	3.3	16	42	2	.0066	.035	−4.34	−3.58
441–445	5.7	29	33	2	.0083	.020	−3.83	−3.68
451–455	6.9	67	25	1	.0121	.023	−3.68	−4.44
461–465	2.2	3	49	1	.0050	.028	−3.50	−3.30
471–475	3.4	8	48	3	.0075	.007	−3.96	−4.56
481–485	3.7	18	53	4	.0058	.020	−3.10	−2.96
491–495	5.0	1	60	2	.0042	.027	−4.05	−4.10
501–505	3.0	17	47	2	.0066	.005	−3.50	−2.77
511–515	2.9	10	58	3	.0058	.037	−3.52	−3.44
521–525	7.5	38	46	2	.0054	.009	−3.37	−2.77
531–535	2.7	85	18	2	.0092	.034	−5.14	−5.32
541–545	5.4	53	51	2	.0066	.039	−2.76	−2.05
551–555	2.8	4	60	2	.0042	.020	−4.25	−4.17
561–565	4.8	47	61	2	.0050	.020	−2.86	−2.14
571–575	3.3	37	64	3	.0063	.025	−3.29	−2.13
581–585	6.0	26	59	2	.0057	.024	−3.10	−3.34
591–595	4.3	21	39	1	.0057	.032	−3.19	−3.30
601–605	2.7	46	36	2	...	.029	−3.49	−3.58
611–615	2.8	27	30	4	.0075	.044	−3.26	−3.09
621–625	5.3	71	23	2	.0083	.032	−3.32	−2.04
631–635	3.4	96	19	2	.0075	.055	−3.86	−3.30
641–645	2.3	80	27	3	.0075	.035	−3.87	−4.25
651–655	4.2	74	27	2	.0075	.052	−2.76	−2.49

APPENDIX I. (CONTINUED)

Time interval T_o+x (in years)	Thickness (in mm)	Color index	Percent CaCO_3	Percent MgCO_3	Percent Kjeldahl nitrogen	Percent tannic acid	d C^{13}	d O^{18}
661–665	2.7	89	21	1	.0054	.057	−3.05	−2.84
671–675	4.5	78	29	1	.0095	.044	−2.90	−2.20
681–685	4.5	90	16	2	.0100	.064	..	..
691–695	3.8	72	27	3	.0100	.053	−4.26	−2.69
701–705	1.8	88	18	3	.0105	.055	−4.21	−5.50
711–715	1.8	32	37	3	.0100	.044	−3.19	−2.63
721–725	4.9	61	24	2	.0066	.050	−3.94	−4.16
731–735	3.9	66	27	2	.0075	.029	−3.34	−3.16
741–745	4.7*	109	12†		.0092	.049	−3.88	−2.37
751–755	4.6	108	9	.. 2	.0145	.078	..	..
761–765	6.1	111	13†	.. 2	.0100	.074	−4.22	−4.55
771–775	4.5	105	13	2	.0095	.069	−4.43	−4.72
781–785	6.4	102	14†	..	.0083	.092	−4.96	−7.48
791–795	4.7	99	14	3	.0087	.037	−4.17	−4.34
801–805	4.3	110	14†	..	.0092	.069	−4.67	−5.76
811–815	4.7	101	10	.. 2	.0100	.046	−4.75	−6.40
821–825	4.2	63	26†	..	.0071	.044	−3.69	−2.12
831–835	2.8	98	14†	..	.0100	.030	−4.62	−5.03
841–845	3.7	88	25†	..	.0087	.049	−4.28	−2.66
851–855	4.5	23	28†	..	.0083	.059	−4.15	−3.94
861–865	4.7*	54	33†	..	.0079	.049	−3.75	−3.11
871–875	3.9	28	22†	..	.0079	.047	−3.52	−2.81
881–885	2.7	55	21†	..	.0083	.034	−4.66	−4.52
891–895	4.4	62	30†	..	.0083	.059	−3.69	−3.59
901–905	5.8	103	14†	..	.0118	.055	−4.43	−4.72
911–915	4.0	57	34†	..	.0075	.059	−3.76	−3.87
921–925	5.3	97	25†	..	.0095	.077	−4.81	−5.99
931–935	7.6	75	30†	..	.0083	.089	−4.34	−4.68
941–945	3.5	100	30†	..	.0134	.049	−4.49	−3.50

Time interval T_o+x (in years)	Thickness (in mm)	Color index	Percent CaCO$_3$	Percent MgCO$_3$	Percent Kjeldahl nitrogen	Percent tannic acid	d C^{13}	d O^{18}
951–955	5.0	56	29†	...	.0063	.035	−4.38	−4.49
961–965	6.4	11	58†	...	.0050	.025	−4.59	−4.68
971–975	3.8	2	63†	...	.0045	.025	−4.83	−4.68
981–985	5.8	5	63†	...	.0045	.019	−4.82	−4.58
986–1005	13.4	14	53†	...	.0079	.030	−4.57	−4.42
1006–1025	18.1	19	38†	...	.0066	.035	−3.91	−3.85
1026–1045	18.9	64	23†	...	.0108	.064	−4.06	−3.72
1046–1065	19.1	93	21†	...	.0087	.050	−4.55	−5.62
1066–1085	18.7	86	24†	...	.0075	.037	−3.75	−3.25
1086–1105	20.5	82	28†	...	.0108	.025	−4.45	−5.08
1106–1125	18.2	76	37†	...	.0118	.034	−4.02	−3.93
1126–1145	18.5	94	24†	...	.0105	.030	−3.72	−3.76
1146–1165	19.4	50	32†	...	.0100	.025	−4.13	−4.01
1166–1185	15.2	51	32†	...	.0079	.020	−4.47	−4.38
1186–1205	18.6	60	49†	...	.0058	.010	−4.25	−4.27
1206–1225	18.1	79	39†	...	.0113	.027	−5.31	−6.88
1226–1245	18.1	39	42†	...	.0092	.020	...	...
1246–1265	15.0	36	50†	...	.0075	.025	...	...
1266–1285	15.1	81	22†	...	.0118	.025	...	...
1286–1305	15.6	59	33†	...	.0092	.035	...	...
1306–1325	19.7	92	22†	...	.0079	.030	−3.70	−3.72
1326–1345	19.2	95	25†	...	.0105	.059	−5.79	−6.60
1346–1365	20.8	69	27†	...	.0100	.032	−1.46	−0.32
1366–1385	19.7	65	27†	...	.0105	.019	−3.09	−2.71
1386–1405	22.4*	45	32†	...	.0092	.040	−3.84	−3.87

*Thickness partially derived by extrapolation.

†Determination by differential thermal analysis. Other CaCO$_3$ determination by titration.

APPENDIX II

Appendix II lists the thickness in millimeters of the individual varves in the Rita Blanca series. The technique employed in measuring the varves is as follows. The varved section was photographed in the field from a distance of about 18 inches using a Polaroid Land camera. Samples were collected, and the section was reconstructed in the laboratory using the overlapping field photographs as a check. The laboratory sections were ground and polished at right angles to the bedding, and the sequence of varves was photographed with a 35-mm single-lens reflex camera with extension tubes. The film image was approximately the same size as the object. The negatives were enlarged so that the final print was 12.2 times larger than the original subject. Measuring was done on 120 9 x 6-inch photographs in conjunction with observations of polished sections under a binocular microscope. At four short intervals within the varve series ($T_0 + 19$ to $T_0 + 25$, $T_0 + 739$ to $T_0 + 745$, $T_0 + 856$ to $T_0 + 870$, and $T_0 + 1264$ to $T_0 + 1268$), the lamination has been wholly or partially effaced. The time interval involved has been estimated using average thickness data.

Thickness (in mm) of the Rita Blanca Varve Series

Couplet No.	0	1	2	3	4	5	6	7	8	9
0	..	1.64	0.98	1.43	1.63	0.86	0.53	0.90	0.98	0.98
10	0.82	1.23	1.07	1.56	1.31	1.15	0.33	0.37	0.61	..
20	..	..	..	..	..	..	1.31	0.98	1.56	1.64
30	2.25	2.87	1.52	1.19	0.53	1.43	0.98	0.74	0.90	0.94
40	0.86	0.74	0.29	0.41	0.74	1.15	1.48	1.02	0.90	0.82
50	0.82	0.77	0.86	0.82	1.07	1.35	1.12	1.07	1.80	1.31
60	0.49	1.52	1.56	1.23	1.23	0.90	1.07	0.74	0.90	0.66
70	0.53	1.12	0.78	0.61	1.19	0.74	1.15	0.61	0.41	0.82
80	0.61	1.02	0.53	0.74	0.57	0.74	1.31	0.66	0.57	0.61
90	0.82	0.90	0.78	0.94	1.72	2.25	0.98	0.94	1.31	0.86
100	0.53	0.66	0.53	1.10	0.66	0.53	0.41	0.66	0.33	0.53
110	0.66	0.66	1.02	2.30	1.12	0.74	1.07	0.66	1.27	1.48
120	0.86	1.11	1.15	0.98	0.78	0.98	2.46	1.56	0.82	0.98
130	1.64	1.23	0.98	0.98	1.60	0.49	0.94	0.53	1.76	0.74
140	0.70	1.02	0.61	1.39	1.43	1.27	0.74	0.78	0.86	0.94
150	0.66	0.74	0.82	0.78	0.66	0.53	0.82	0.45	0.82	0.74
160	0.41	0.94	0.41	0.53	0.41	0.53	0.78	0.41	0.53	0.82
170	0.45	1.64	0.57	0.78	0.49	0.78	0.37	0.86	0.41	0.49
180	0.66	1.11	0.41	0.37	0.57	1.72	1.31	0.57	0.90	1.31
190	1.07	0.61	0.57	0.57	0.78	0.98	0.49	0.86	0.78	1.23
200	0.66	0.74	0.78	0.53	0.45	0.41	0.45	0.33	0.33	0.74
210	0.62	0.66	0.53	0.53	0.57	1.11	0.41	0.70	0.70	0.70
220	1.11	1.31	0.62	0.98	1.07	0.70	0.98	0.78	0.66	0.66
230	0.74	0.94	0.82	0.94	0.53	0.78	1.23	0.82	0.78	0.41
240	0.41	0.33	0.37	0.98	0.74	1.07	0.90	0.66	0.74	1.23
250	1.23	1.07	0.86	0.74	1.02	1.07	1.11	0.94	1.02	0.94
260	0.57	1.15	1.48	0.53	0.90	1.72	1.15	1.91	1.23	1.48
270	1.52	1.52	1.35	1.35	1.31	1.48	0.70	1.19	1.35	0.78
280	0.90	0.70	0.82	1.15	1.31	0.86	0.78	0.29	0.98	0.57
290	0.49	0.37	0.41	2.87	0.66	0.74	0.94	0.66	0.94	1.23
300	0.41	0.82	0.66	0.45	1.31	1.15	1.60	1.27	0.82	0.53
310	0.49	0.41	0.82	0.78	0.41	0.74	0.78	1.80	0.53	0.49
320	0.62	0.62	0.57	0.25	0.33	0.41	0.33	1.39	0.74	0.98
330	0.66	1.56	0.49	0.86	0.74	0.90	0.70	0.94	0.41	0.49
340	0.16	0.16	0.25	0.37	0.66	0.33	0.74	0.37	0.37	0.41

Couplet No.	0	1	2	3	4	5	6	7	8	9
350	0.82	0.41	0.33	0.29	1.56	0.25	0.29	0.57	2.05	0.53
360	0.37	0.74	0.66	0.57	0.57	2.62	0.74	1.07	1.72	0.82
370	0.66	1.80	0.98	0.98	0.57	1.62	1.23	0.82	1.07	0.74
380	0.82	0.86	1.86	0.62	0.74	0.74	0.66	0.41	0.94	0.33
390	0.57	1.15	0.74	0.98	0.53	0.49	1.64	0.78	0.74	0.90
400	0.74	2.13	1.02	0.78	0.33	0.82	0.41	0.41	0.74	0.82
410	0.29	0.25	0.74	0.49	1.97	0.53	0.41	0.57	0.94	0.37
420	0.37	0.37	1.07	0.74	0.74	2.21	0.82	0.70	0.90	1.19
430	0.90	0.57	1.07	0.41	0.86	0.41	0.37	0.94	0.25	0.37
440	0.41	0.33	3.03	0.74	0.49	1.11	1.35	1.60	1.31	0.90
450	0.98	0.90	0.82	1.60	1.48	2.13	0.82	1.39	0.98	0.25
460	0.16	0.20	0.20	0.41	0.62	0.78	0.94	0.66	0.57	0.82
470	0.78	0.74	0.37	0.62	0.98	0.66	0.82	0.70	0.49	0.33
480	0.41	0.78	1.19	0.49	0.41	0.82	1.56	0.45	0.49	0.57
490	0.33	0.29	0.41	0.57	1.80	1.97	0.49	0.74	0.66	0.33
500	0.66	0.78	0.57	0.70	0.49	0.49	1.56	0.12	0.16	0.41
510	0.49	0.74	0.74	0.37	0.37	0.66	0.90	0.37	0.57	0.66
520	1.56	3.40	0.49	0.33	0.98	2.25	0.33	0.37	0.45	0.49
530	0.74	1.48	0.29	0.25	0.41	0.29	0.41	0.41	0.37	0.41
540	0.74	1.31	1.80	0.98	0.57	0.74	0.66	1.39	0.90	0.49
550	0.82	0.62	0.49	0.41	0.82	0.49	0.49	1.80	0.49	0.98
560	0.57	0.74	1.39	0.74	0.82	1.15	1.97	1.31	2.17	2.46
570	0.74	0.57	0.90	0.62	0.49	0.74	0.66	1.52	0.74	0.94
580	2.09	1.97	0.49	0.37	2.38	0.74	0.57	1.12	2.62	1.19
590	0.78	0.90	0.82	1.11	0.49	0.98	0.90	1.48	0.57	0.29
600	0.57	0.37	0.45	0.41	0.53	0.98	0.82	0.70	0.41	0.74
610	0.49	0.49	0.49	0.41	0.78	0.62	0.86	1.39	0.45	0.57
620	0.41	1.23	2.38	0.82	0.49	0.37	0.33	0.49	0.70	0.74
630	0.98	0.98	0.66	0.66	0.66	0.41	0.49	0.74	0.98	1.02
640	0.49	0.66	0.37	0.37	0.49	0.41	0.49	0.57	0.49	0.25
650	0.29	0.37	0.53	0.86	1.56	0.90	0.49	1.11	0.53	0.25
660	0.29	0.53	0.41	0.33	1.07	0.37	0.94	0.57	0.33	0.45
670	0.66	0.49	1.80	1.48	0.45	0.25	0.33	0.94	0.45	0.25
680	0.41	0.33	0.25	1.64	1.72	0.53	0.37	0.98	0.37	0.33
690	0.57	0.53	0.74	0.29	1.31	0.94	0.90	0.90	0.57	1.07
700	0.20	0.33	0.16	0.20	0.57	0.49	0.33	0.41	1.64	0.16
710	0.12	0.25	0.16	0.41	0.57	0.37	0.37	0.74	0.66	1.27
720	0.78	0.70	1.19	1.15	0.57	1.27	0.53	1.23	0.94	1.56
730	1.15	0.41	0.53	0.49	0.78	1.72	0.70	0.57	0.49	..
740	..	..	..	..	..	..	0.57	0.74	2.95	0.94
750	0.94	0.90	0.74	0.74	1.15	1.07	0.66	0.70	0.86	0.98
760	0.53	1.39	0.98	1.48	0.70	1.56	1.07	0.78	0.41	0.37
770	0.57	1.39	0.70	0.57	0.90	0.98	0.90	2.38	1.39	0.62
780	1.15	1.31	1.23	1.15	0.98	1.76	0.90	0.66	0.62	0.74
790	1.35	1.23	1.07	0.98	0.74	0.66	0.66	0.82	0.98	1.68
800	0.90	0.90	0.66	1.15	0.86	0.70	0.74	1.43	0.66	1.31
810	0.37	1.68	0.74	0.37	1.31	0.37	0.49	0.49	1.39	0.90
820	1.07	0.86	0.49	1.56	0.41	0.90	1.89	0.49	1.48	0.41
830	0.90	0.66	0.49	0.82	0.49	0.29	0.41	1.39	0.98	0.57
840	0.86	0.90	0.33	0.29	1.07	1.07	0.90	0.57	1.23	0.74
850	0.98	0.94	0.49	0.49	0.41	2.21	..	..	..	..
860	..	..	..	..	..	..	..	..	..	..
870	..	0.45	1.39	0.37	0.53	1.15	0.33	1.89	0.45	0.49
880	0.33	0.41	0.41	0.45	0.62	0.78	0.45	0.53	0.62	1.39
890	0.41	0.41	1.39	0.57	0.90	1.15	1.15	0.66	0.49	0.74

Couplet No.	0	1	2	3	4	5	6	7	8	9
900	0.74	0.66	0.66	0.66	2.46	1.39	2.05	0.70	0.25	0.16
910	0.37	0.25	1.48	0.74	0.66	0.82	0.66	0.78	1.64	1.64
920	0.98	1.64	0.25	2.54	0.57	0.33	2.83	0.62	0.57	0.41
930	1.39	1.48	1.64	0.74	1.31	2.46	0.98	0.66	1.56	2.87
940	1.64	0.57	0.49	0.57	1.15	0.74	0.90	0.49	0.66	2.87
950	0.82	1.80	1.80	0.74	0.29	0.41	2.54	1.15	0.98	0.74
960	1.23	2.21	0.33	1.97	0.90	0.98	1.97	1.02	0.86	1.19
970	0.74	1.97	1.31	0.16	0.16	0.20	0.41	0.41	0.45	1.07
980	0.25	0.41	2.50	1.02	0.37	1.52	1.56	1.15	1.15	1.35
990	0.49	0.25	0.57	1.56	0.66	0.45	0.62	0.66	0.37	0.33
1000	0.29	0.29	0.33	0.57	0.33	0.37	0.66	1.80	0.70	0.37
1010	0.29	0.41	0.33	0.37	0.82	0.66	0.94	0.74	1.23	1.39
1020	1.07	1.68	1.80	1.02	0.90	0.90	0.82	1.15	1.56	1.39
1030	0.66	2.05	0.66	0.70	0.62	0.86	1.43	0.70	0.57	0.57
1040	0.45	0.66	0.49	1.31	0.94	1.31	0.49	1.11	1.23	0.78
1050	0.86	1.15	1.23	0.33	1.89	0.66	0.66	1.93	1.11	0.57
1060	0.94	1.68	0.74	0.41	0.45	0.86	0.98	0.94	0.74	0.57
1070	0.94	0.70	1.15	0.45	1.43	0.82	1.84	0.53	0.98	0.82
1080	0.98	0.90	0.70	1.02	1.23	1.02	0.78	0.74	0.86	1.11
1090	0.98	1.60	0.98	1.39	0.86	1.11	1.19	1.60	0.82	0.82
1100	0.98	1.02	0.74	0.82	1.07	1.07	0.66	0.74	0.74	2.79
1110	0.86	0.62	2.50	1.19	0.49	1.23	0.57	0.70	0.66	0.53
1120	0.74	0.70	0.70	0.74	0.66	0.41	0.37	0.74	1.15	0.90
1130	1.02	0.70	1.02	1.60	0.74	0.78	1.39	0.78	1.56	0.66
1140	1.64	0.53	0.49	0.98	0.90	0.53	0.90	1.23	1.76	0.49
1150	2.13	1.07	1.02	1.39	0.78	0.41	0.25	1.64	1.07	1.19
1160	1.89	0.70	0.33	0.37	0.33	0.41	0.37	0.74	0.33	1.15
1170	0.25	0.74	1.31	2.01	1.31	0.94	0.53	0.78	0.90	0.90
1180	0.90	1.48	0.16	0.12	0.16	0.16	0.25	0.53	0.37	1.31
1190	1.72	1.07	1.80	0.74	0.66	0.29	1.23	0.66	0.37	1.23
1200	0.62	1.19	0.74	0.90	2.05	0.82	0.74	1.52	0.37	0.33
1210	0.90	1.39	1.48	0.57	1.48	0.82	0.82	0.37	1.31	0.74
1220	1.02	0.94	0.49	0.49	0.62	1.72	0.41	1.97	1.93	1.97
1230	0.66	0.49	1.19	0.78	1.64	1.07	0.70	0.49	0.57	0.49
1240	0.45	0.45	0.82	0.41	0.70	0.86	0.41	0.62	0.82	2.13
1250	0.62	0.49	0.78	0.98	0.41	0.53	0.70	0.62	0.90	0.82
1260	0.37	0.57	0.86	0.53	..	..	..	..	..	1.11
1270	0.70	0.62	0.78	0.29	0.53	1.23	0.82	0.74	0.57	0.74
1280	0.78	0.82	0.78	0.78	0.57	0.49	0.74	0.78	0.66	0.62
1290	0.25	0.57	0.53	0.53	0.94	0.74	1.15	0.82	1.23	0.78
1300	0.94	0.74	0.66	0.57	1.07	1.27	0.66	0.57	2.30	1.07
1310	0.78	0.82	0.98	2.13	0.98	0.53	0.82	0.98	0.82	1.23
1320	1.23	0.53	0.98	0.82	0.66	0.82	1.19	0.66	0.49	1.07
1330	1.23	0.74	0.74	1.15	1.72	1.15	1.60	1.11	0.49	0.78
1340	0.82	1.19	0.86	1.07	0.57	0.57	0.74	1.39	1.35	1.07
1350	0.57	1.64	0.74	0.66	0.62	0.90	1.11	0.98	0.74	0.90
1360	1.15	1.02	0.74	0.66	1.31	2.54	0.78	0.74	0.49	0.86
1370	1.52	1.56	1.56	1.68	0.74	1.64	0.62	0.66	1.11	0.94
1380	0.66	0.57	1.84	0.41	0.70	0.78	0.82	0.66	1.23	0.45
1390	0.45	0.66	1.07	1.02	1.84	0.82	1.27	1.31	1.97	1.97
1400	2.46	0.70								

Index

Subject Index

achene, 105, 172
air masses, 154, 155
algae, 24, 28, 77, 85, 148
   (*see also Botryococcus* and
   Pediastrum)
alkalinity, 106, 110-113, 120, 138, 144,
   145, 153
altitudinal succession, 88, 90
aragonite, 25, 27

bi-spectral analysis (*see* cross spectra
   analysis)
big sagebrush, 86, 151, 152, 153, 155
   (*see Artemisia tridentata*)
Blancan, 1, 3, 6, 7, 77, 78, 83, 88, 90, 92,
   93, 94, 142, 151, 154, 155
Blanco Formation, 5, 6, 7, 8

caddis fly cases, 118, 147
calcium carbonate, 15, 19-21, 25-28, 36,
   38, 41, 42, 44, 51, 52, 59, 62, 66, 68,
   69-71, 72-75, 90, 91, 92, 94, 142,
   145, 147, 148, 149, 150, 151, 154,
   155, 165, 200-203
caprock, 5, 9, 10, 11, 142, 143
carbon isotopes (*see* isotopes)
Cenozoic stratigraphy, 7
chaparral, 88
chemical stratification (*see* meromixis)
chlorides, 92, 145
clay, 15, 19-21, 28, 29, 36, 38, 41, 42, 59,
   62, 66, 68, 69-71, 72-75, 147, 149,
   150, 151, 154, 155, 165
climate, 9, 10, 89, 90, 93, 94, 105, 142,
   149, 151-155
climatic changes, 57, 94, 151, 154, 165
coherence, coefficients of, 70
color, 19, 38, 59, 68, 69-71, 147, 148,
   200-203
color index, 38, 40, 68, 69, 165
correlation coefficient, 19, 52, 59, 66, 68
cottonwood (*see Populus*)
cross-spectra, 66, 72

cycles
   annual, 15-20, 29-37, 147-149
   climatic, 154, 155
   lithologic, 15-20, 38-44, 154
   long term, 16, 38-44, 53-58, 63, 142,
      148, 164, 165
   22-year, 62-67, 72, 150

deflation basin, 5, 6, 8, 9, 99, 141, 142,
   143, 146
diatoms, 30
differential thermal analysis, 24, 25, 26,
   41, 44, 52, 165
dragonfly nymphs, 77, 118, 147
   (*see* Odonata)
dy-type sediment, 23, 148

ecosystem, 150
epilimnion, 28, 149
evaporation, 33, 51, 52, 57, 90, 93, 148

fishes, 20, 78, 135-140, 143, 144, 197
   (*see also Lepomis, Fundulus*)
floral associations, 89
fossil flora, 97-106, 168, 171, 172
   microstratigraphic position, 31
Fourier spectrum, 60, 62, 63, 64, 65
frost-free period, 89, 93
fungi, saprolegnian? spores, 22, 146, 149,
   154

gastropods, 12
geologic setting, 3
glacial maximum, 153
glaciers, continental, 5, 93
grass (*see* Gramineae)
grass cover, 143, 149, 155
Great Basin, 86, 88, 93, 132, 151, 152,
   155

harmonic analysis, 59
Hartley County, 3, 4, 5, 6, 131, 132

209

High Plains, 5, 6, 8, 87, 141, 142, 145, 151
humic matter, 23
hypolimnion, 113, 147

ice cover, 148, 153
Illinoian, 7, 153
illite, 24, 26, 28, 44, 148, 154
insects, 5, 20, 22, 31, 32, 77, 117-133, 143-145, 147, 152
    aquatic, 20, 44, 117-122, 144, 145
    terrestrial, 22, 123-133, 131, 143, 152
isotopes, carbon and oxygen, 33, 41, 47-58, 59, 68, 69, 147, 151, 157, 165, 200-203

juniper, 87, 89, 90, 93
    (see Juniperus)

Kansan, 6, 7, 10
kaolin, 29, 44, 148, 154
killifish (see Fundulus)
Kjeldahl nitrogen, 25, 38, 43, 59, 68, 69-71, 165, 200-203

lake deposits (see Rita Blanca)
leaves, 23, 31, 77, 88, 97-106, 143, 144, 153, 168-173
lithologic cycles (see cycles)

magnesium carbonate, 25-27, 38, 41, 200-203
mammals, 6, 8, 144
Meade Formation, 8
meloid beetles, 123, 126
    (see also Lytta and Epicauta)
meromixis, 117, 120, 121, 122, 144, 145, 146, 150, 153
midges, 32, 37, 117-121, 144
    (see also Chironominidae)
    microstratigraphic position, 31, 32
monimolimnion, 117, 146
moss spores, 33, 34, 148, 166
    (see also Musci?)
    position in laminae, 31, 33, 34

Nebraskan, 5, 7, 8, 99
nitrogen (see Kjeldahl nitrogen)

oak (see Quercus)
    Gambel's, 31, 33, 86, 88, 143, 169
    post, 31, 86, 97, 98, 99, 169
    scrub, 89, 90
    shinnery, 152
Ogallala Group, 5, 6, 7, 8, 10, 11, 85, 86, 142, 152
organic matter, 19-25, 36, 41, 44, 68, 146
    (see Kjeldahl nitrogen, tannin-lignin, dy, sapropel)

ostracodes, 28, 30, 31, 36, 37, 77, 144, 147, 148, 149, 152, 192-195, 198
    (see also Lymnocythere, Cyprideis, Candona, Ilyocypris)
    living, 110
    microstratigraphic position of, 30, 31
    nodosity, 110
    seasonal periodicity of, 30, 112, 113
oxygen isotopes (see isotopes)

paleoecology, 141-157
paleontology, 77-139
Pearlette ash, 6, 7, 10, 11
pelecypods, 198
petrology, 15-75
phase angle, 74
plankton, 20, 23, 144
plant fragments, 22, 30, 147, 148, 163
pollen, 22-23, 78, 83-95, 166-169
    modern, 85
    microstratigraphic variation, 31, 33, 34
    profile, 83-95, 151
    processing, 83
    sedimentation rate, 22
    systematic descriptions, 86-88
power spectra, 60, 66
precipitation, 58, 89, 90, 93, 149, 150, 151, 153, 154, 155
pyrite, 146

rate of deposition
    "absolute," 39, 41, 42
    of varves, 17, 142
reptiles, 93
riparian community, 88, 93, 97, 99, 103, 104, 105, 143, 144, 151
Rita Blanca Lake
    age, 6-8
    basin, origin of, 8-10
    changes with time, 10, 147
    environs, 143-144
    flora and fauna, 77-81
    location, 3, 4
    sediments, 6, 10-12, 29, 41, 147
    setting in time and place, 141, 142
    type of lake, 144
Rita Blanca lake deposits
    age, 6-8
    extent, 10-12
    geologic setting, 3-13
    location, 4
    paleoecology, 141-157
    paleontology, 77-140
    petrology, 15-75

sagebrush (see also Artemisia and big sagebrush), 33, 86, 88, 89, 90, 143, 151, 152, 155

salinity, 102, 106, 110-113, 120, 138, 144, 145, 147, 152
sand, 5, 7, 9, 11, 16, 85, 143, 147
Sappa Member, 8
sapropel, 23, 30
seasonal changes, 30, 31, 32, 33, 37, 51, 112, 147-149
silt, 19-21, 29, 31, 36, 41, 44, 85, 143, 147, 148, 149, 153, 154, 155
soil, 5, 9, 23, 85, 86, 89, 113, 142, 143
spectra
  cross, 72
  power, 69
spores
  musci?, 33, 34, 148, 166
  saprolegnian?, 22, 146, 148, 149, 154
statistical analysis, 59-75
stratigraphic column, 16
sulfates, 29, 92, 145
sunfish (*see Leopomis*)
systematic list, 77-81

Tahoka Clay, 6, 7
tannic acid, 26, 200-203
tannin-lignin, 25, 26, 38, 41, 43, 59, 68, 69-71, 148, 165

temperature, 89, 90, 92, 93, 94, 150, 153, 154, 155
time-series analysis, 59
Tule Formation, 6, 7, 8
turbidity currents, 36, 147

varves, 15, 46, 142, 147, 148, 149, 150, 161, 162, 164
  changes with time, 31, 147, 148, 149
  composition and origin, 15-46
  correlation, 17, 19, 20, 22, 150, 162
  "doubling," 24
  evidence for annual nature, 29-37, 51-52
  frequency distribution, 17, 18
  localities, 11
  petrology, 15-29
  Recent, 23, 33, 35
  thickness, 38, 39, 59, 62, 66, 68, 142, 149, 156, 200, 204-206

weevils, 131-133, 143, 152
  (*see also Cleonus*)
willow (*see Salix*)

Systematic Index

(*See also* **Systematic List, p. 77**)

Abies, 87, 93, 144
Acalyptratae, 127
Acer, 85, 87, 144
   A. saccharum, 85
Aedes, 118
Aeshnidae, 118
Aleocharinae, 126, 182, 183
Alismaceae, 101
Alnus, 87, 144
Amaranthaceae, 33, 84, 151, 166
Ambrosia, 132
Amelanchier, 88
Amorpha, 104, 144, 172-173
   A. laevigata, 104, 144, 172, 173
Apoidea, 129, 188, 189
Areopodidae, 125
Artemisia, 31, 33, 37, 77, 83, 84, 85, 86,
   88, 90, 91, 92, 93, 94, 98, 99, 132,
   143, 144, 147, 151, 152, 153, 168,
   169
   A. filifolia, 152
   A. tridentata, 86, 132, 143, 152
Astragalus, 132
Atheriniformes, 135

Baccharis, 105, 144, 172, 173
   B. salicina, 105, 144, 172, 173
Betula, 87, 144
Bombyliidae, 127, 184, 185
Botryococcus, 20, 24, 77, 80, 84, 85, 90,
   91, 92, 94, 144, 147
Braconidae, 128, 186
Brassica, 87
Calyptratae, 127, 186, 187
Candona, 30, 31, 37, 108, 109, 144, 148,
   192, 193
   C. crogmania, 109
   C. crogmaniana, 111
   C. nyensis, 110
Carabidae, 125, 185, 186
Carya, 87
Celtis, 85, 87, 144

Cenchrus, 102, 143, 170, 171
   C. pauciflorus, 102, 143, 170, 171
Centrarchidae, 137
Cercocarpus, 88
   C. parvifolius, 88
Cheliomyrmicini, 188, 189
Chenopodiaceae, 33, 84, 85, 87, 93, 151,
   166
Chironomidae, 32, 117, 118, 178, 179,
   182, 183
Chironomus, 31, 32, 77, 117, 119, 120,
   144, 145, 177, 178, 179, 180, 181
   C. bathophilus, 121
   C. defectus, 121
   C. (chironomus) kirklandi, 117, 119,
      120, 144, 145, 177, 178, 179, 180,
      181
   C. noctivaga, 119, 120
   C. taurica, 119
Chrysomelidae, 127
Cicadellidae, 125, 182, 185
Cleonus, 131, 132, 143, 152, 190, 191
   C. channingensis, 132, 143, 190, 191
   C. circumductus, 132
   C. ritablancaensis, 131, 143, 190, 191
   C. stratus, 132
Coccinellidae, 126, 174, 175
?Coenagrionidae, 118, 174
Coleoptera, 125, 130, 131, 182, 183, 184,
   185, 186, 190, 191
Compositae, 33, 84, 85, 86, 95, 151, 166
Coniferales, 33
Coreidae, 124, 182, 183
Corizidae, 124, 182, 183
Corylus, 87
Crataegus, 104, 144, 172-173
   C. chrysocarpa?, 104, 144, 172, 173
Croton, 85, 87
Cruciferae, 87
Culex, 118, 144, 176, 177
Culicidae, *Culex*, 118, 177
Curculionidae, 131

213

Cyprideis, 30, 31, 37, 77, 108, 109, 144,
    147, 148, 192, 193, 194, 195
  C. littoralis, 109
  C. mexicana, 110
  C. salebrosa, 109, 110
Cyprinodontidae, 135

Deltocephalinae, 182, 183
Dicotyledoneae, 103
Diplotaxis, 126, 184, 185
Diptera, 32, 118, 127, 176-177, 182, 183,
    184, 185, 186, 187, 190, 191
Disonycha, 127
Dorylinae, 128, 188, 189
Dysdercus, 124

Elaeagnus, 87
Ephedra, 87, 144, 166
Epicauta, 126
Equus (Plesippus), 6
  E. simplicidens, 6
Eriogonum, 87
Euphrobia, 85, 87

Formicidae, 128, 129, 188, 189
Fraxinus, 87, 144
Fulgoroidea, 125
Fundulus, 77, 135, 136, 137, 138, 143,
    144, 196, 197
  F. detillai, 136, 137
  F. kansae, 136, 137, 143
  F. sternbergi, 136, 137, 138
  F. zebrinus, 135, 136, 137, 143, 144,
    196, 197

Gigantocamelus, 6
  G. spatulus, 6
Gramineae, 33, 77, 84, 86, 90, 91, 92, 93,
    94, 151, 155, 166

Halliella, 120
Hemiptera, 124, 182, 183
Heterocypris, 110
Hippodamia, 126
  H. convergens, 126
Homoptera, 125, 182, 183, 184, 185
Hymenoclea, 132
Hymenoptera, 128, 129, 186, 187, 188,
    189, 190, 191

Ichneumonidae, 128, 129, 186, 187
Ilyocypridae?, 198, 199
Ilyocypris, 30, 108

Juglans, 85, 144
Juniperus, 84, 85, 87, 93, 144, 153, 166

Leguminoseae, 87
Lepomis, 135, 137, 138, 144, 196, 197
  L. megalotis, 137, 138, 144

Leptocoris, 124
Libellulidae, 77, 114, 118, 174, 175
Liguliflorae, 86
Limnocythere, 30, 31, 37, 77, 107, 108,
    144, 147, 148, 192, 193, 194, 195
  L. africana, 110
  L. friabilis, 109
  L. incisa, 109
  L. inopinata, 109
  L. sanctipatricii, 109, 110 111
  L. staplini, 109, 110
Lygaeidae, 124, 182, 183
Lygaeus, 124
Lytta, 126, 184, 185
  L. (Paralytta) deserticolor, 126

Maclura, 104, 144, 172
  M. pomifera, 104, 144, 172, 173
Malvaceae, 85, 87
Meloidae, 126, 185
Mimosa, 85
?Molannidae, 118, 177
Monocotyledoneae, 101
Musci?, 106
Myrmicinae, 128, 188, 189
Myzinum, 128

Najadaceae, 101
Nannippus, 6
  N. phlegon, 6
Nysius?, 124, 182, 183

Odonata, 118, 147, 174, 175
Onagraceae, 87
Oncopeltus, 124
?Orthocladiinae, 120, 181
Oscillatoria, 24
  O. rubescens, 24
Osteichthyes, 135

Panicum, 102, 143, 170, 171
  P. dichotomiflorum?, 102, 143, 170,
    171
Pediastrum, 20, 85, 144, 147
Perciformes, 137
Phaedon, 127
Physa, 12, 79
Picea, 85, 87, 93, 144, 153
Pinus, 84, 86, 93, 144, 153, 166
Pisidium?, 79, 198, 199
Polemoniaceae, 87
Pompilidae, 129, 188, 189, 190, 191
Populus, 31, 87, 103, 144, 172, 173
  P. deltoides?, 31, 85, 144, 172, 173
  P. sargentii, 103
Portulacaceae, 85
Prosopis, 85
  P. juliflora, 85
Prunus, 85, 104, 144
  P. virginiana, 85

Pyrrhocoridae, 124

Quercus, 31, 33, 77, 84, 85, 86, 88, 90,
    91, 92, 93, 97, 98, 99, 143, 147, 152,
    166, 168-171
  Q. gambelii, 31, 86, 97, 98, 99, 143,
    168-169
  Q. havardii, 98, 152
  Q. lyrata, 98, 143
  Q. margaretta, 98
  Q. pungens, 98
  Q. ritablancensis, 97, 98, 143, 168-169,
    170-171
  Q. stellata, 31, 86, 97, 98, 99, 143,
    168-169

Rhamnus, 105
Ribes, 104, 144
Rosaceae, 87
Ruppia, 20, 102, 106, 144, 145, 170, 171
  R. maritima, 102, 144, 145, 170, 171

Salix, 31, 77, 78, 103, 144, 147, 170, 173
  S. bebbiana?, 31, 103, 144, 170-173
  S. caroliniana, 103
  S. exigua, 31, 103, 144, 170-173

Sapindus, 104, 144, 172, 173
  S. drummondii?, 104, 144, 173
Sapotaceae, 87
Sarcobatus, 87, 144
Scarabaeidae, 126, 185
Schizophora, 127, 185, 186
Selaginella, 83, 87, 144
Selenophorus, 125, 185, 186
Sheperdia, 87
Sparganium, 101, 144, 170, 171
Staphylinidae, 126, 182, 183
Stegmastodon, 6
Syrphidae, 127, 186, 187
Syrphus, 127, 186, 187

?Tanypodinae, 120, 182, 183
?Tanytarsus, 120
Tidestromia, 87
Tingidae, 124, 182, 183
Tiphiidae, 128
Trichoptera, 118, 176, 177
Tubuliflorae, 86, 166, 167
Typha, 87, 144

Ulmus, 85, 87, 144
Umbelliferae, 85, 87